£5
09|2020

# True Blue Superglue

NOVELS BY THE SAME AUTHOR

*Thoughts in a Makeshift Mortuary* (1989)

*The Sweet-Smelling Jasmine* (1993)

*Video Dreams* (1995)

*The Telling of Angus Quain* (1997)

*Kitchen Boy* (2011)

*The Miracle of Crocodile Flats* (2012)

*Napoleon Bones* (2013)

# True Blue Superglue

*Jenny Hobbs*

Published in 2015 by Umuzi
an imprint of Penguin Random House South Africa (Pty) Ltd
Company Reg No 1953/000441/07
Estuaries No 4, Oxbow Crescent, Century Avenue,
Century City, 7441, South Africa
PO Box 1144, Cape Town, 8000, South Africa
umuzi@randomstruik.co.za
www.randomstruik.co.za

© 2015 Jenny Hobbs

All rights reserved.
No part of this book may be reproduced or transmitted in any form or by any means, mechanical or electronic, including photocopying and recording, or be stored in any information storage or retrieval system, without written permission from the publisher.

First edition, first printing 2015
1 3 5 7 9 8 6 4 2

ISBN 978-1-4152-0762-8 (Print)
ISBN 978-1-4152-0652-2 (ePub)
ISBN 978-1-4152-0653-9 (PDF)

Cover design by mr design
Text design by Chérie Collins
Set in 11.5 on 16.5 pt Adobe Caslon Pro

Printed and bound in India by Replika Press Pvt. Ltd.

For Caro, Ducky, Freda, Gael, Mari,
Mare, Marilyn, Pam, Sheila and Vanessa
Those were the days

*Happiness is not what I thought. Happiness is the lucky pane of glass you carry in your head. It takes all your cunning just to hang on to it, and once it's smashed you have to move into a different sort of life.*

– Carol Shields, *Unless*

# I

We were university students in the early sixties, rocking and rolling as we headed for new freedoms: guilt-free sex, miniskirts and sophisticated drinks like screwdrivers and ginger squares.

Doug and I met during my first year and his third. He was twenty-one to my eighteen. Both of us were virgins, nothing unusual then. Like most only sons, he was shy of girls. I wasn't shy of boys. At high school my friends and I had terrorised boys struggling with rampant puberty when they are unable to control gangling limbs and wayward voices. Lifting my head now to gaze at a photo of my son Robin, I hope we didn't do any permanent damage.

Doug had a dream of life's path opening out before him full of promise and possibilities – as long as you kept a goal in sight. He should have been a visionary poet like William Blake or a brooding actor like Ralph Fiennes, never a businessman.

But we were post-war children; commerce beckoned and marriage was as inevitable as scientific progress. By the time we met, polio had been conquered, men had been shot into space, the far side of the moon had been photographed and lasers had been invented. Our marriage seemed a fine union to observers (and it was, it *was* for most of the time).

Our Song was 'Dream a Little Dream of Me'. Frankie Laine, Doris Day and Bing Crosby had all recorded it in the fifties. Bands still played it towards the end of dances when rock 'n' roll and the twist gave way to the smoochy oldies that glued us together: 'Stardust' and 'I'm in the Mood for Love' and 'Goodnight Sweetheart'.

As a mid-century teenager, I had been reared on the syrupy ideal of domestic togetherness, though the vistas opened by university offered the enticing new prospects of careers and independence. Mum is of the generation who just missed being liberated and observes our continuing efforts to be New Women with wry sympathy.

She's a woman of many talents who married young and gave me what she wished she'd had: a stable home, nice things, higher education and endless encouragement.

I'm not sure when she realised that she'd made the wrong choice of husband. The facts are that she had a horror of divorce and there were no more children after me. In the spirit of the times, she knuckled down and made the best of things, throwing herself into good causes, sewing, gardening and holding formal dinner parties for Dad's business colleagues where they told fishing stories that got taller as the whiskies grew stronger.

My parents were profoundly incompatible, though they hung in together for forty years and found a new lease of life towards the end. 'Your mother was a damn fine woman,' he mumbled before heading to the great trout water in the sky.

It was different for me. Determined not to make the same mistake, I married the first congenial man who came my way and we lived happily almost ever after.

# 2

Growing up in South Africa in the fifties had its unique pleasures, but freedom wasn't one of them. Girls didn't walk alone in the streets, go on trains by themselves, choose their own clothes or wear make-up until they were at least sixteen. Teenage parties ended on the stroke of midnight when adamant fathers loomed in the doorway. For best, my friends and I wore demure twinsets and dainty coral or pearl necklaces. When I went into town with Mum for a morning's shopping, we added hats and gloves and carried handbags. Tea at Stuttaford's centred on a tiered cake-stand with triangular sandwiches and iced cup cakes nestled on doilies.

Like other mothers, mine kept a beady eye on my friends, vetoing 'unsuitable' activities. They said it was because they didn't want us to get a fast reputation, but they really meant get pregnant. That prospect kept most of us on the straight and narrow before marriage. Girls didn't want to get stuck with a baby while all their friends went out and had fun; guys didn't want to be trapped in a shotgun marriage by someone looking for a free ride for the rest of her life.

Even the guys who were bold enough to go into a chemist and ask for FLs (condoms were called French Letters then), braving the 'Small? Medium? Large?' questions, kept the increasingly worn foil packets just to show each other. Ominous stories were whispered about leaks or FLs that slipped off in the heat of the moment, condemning users to early parental servitude.

As an only child, I had more than my share of finery: frocks with tight waists and long skirts, waspies, stiff petticoats, spit-on mascara, blue eye shadow, pointy shoes with stiletto heels and handbags to match. And I had a loft bedroom with a black-and-white photo of Marlon Brando looking broodily sexy in a white T-shirt taped to the door of my wardrobe.

The teachers at my school didn't approve of Marlon Brando. The movies shown at the monthly socials were sentimental musicals like *Oklahoma!* or *Brigadoon* or *Singin' in the Rain.* Press-ganged to attend by our mothers, my friends and I sat in the back row loudly chewing gum and mocking the juniors. We were the Fearsome Foursome: Vron, Cuckoo, Jude and Annie. In a gang we were intrepid, though on our own and at home we did what was expected. In the placid fifties girls dreamt of getting married and settling down.

Veronica and Cuckoo had been in my class since primary school: Vron a freckled beanpole who could sit on her hair when it was unplaited, and Cuckoo the joker who could imitate anyone. The other member of the Foursome, Jude (short for Judith), had arrived at the beginning of high school, furious at being sent away from her missionary family in Uganda and farmed out to an aunt for a decent education.

'What's so great about this dump?' she'd demand.

Cuckoo suggested, 'The Museum? The Cathedral? That should suit Your Holiness.'

'Don't be stupid. I hate this bloody place. My aunt makes me sick. Her house stinks of stoep polish and old dogs.'

'And I suppose houses in Uganda don't stink?' Vron couldn't help being superior; she'd caught it from her snobby mother.

'Our house is thatched with palm leaves which smell lovely.'

'I'd be afraid of the savages,' Vron said.

'That's typical of you people! They're not savages, they're Africans.'

'We call ours natives. Anyway, you're English.'

'I'm not! I'm Ugandan. England is the very *last* place I'd ever want to live.'

To keep the peace, I said, 'Mum says England's lovely and she'll take me there one day.'

'That's because you're spoilt rotten, Annie.'

I was. I had enough pocket money to go to the flicks once a week and treat my friends afterwards to banana splits and knickerbocker glories at the milk bar. We had a radiogram in our living room that could stack up to ten long-playing records. They thumped down one by one as the playing arm drew back, hovered, jerked forward, then lowered itself so the needle slipped into the first groove. We had records by the Mills Brothers, Nat King Cole, Doris Day, Dean Martin and all the songs from *South Pacific.* We had a domestic worker and a gardener who lived in the backyard, so I never had to lift a finger.

Being an only child had its downside, though. I was the

focus of Mum's ambitions for me to succeed in a circle of youngsters whose parents were Nice People, to be followed by a spell at university to secure a well-educated husband.

'Try and find someone who doesn't go off fishing all the time,' she said once. 'Men who prefer their friends' company to their wives don't make good husbands. Your father is a case in point.'

'Why did you marry him, then?'

'Because—' She gave me her over-the-specs glare, usually reserved for wrongdoing. 'You want the truth?'

I nodded, bemused. I'd thought she always told the truth.

'Because my old man was a bully, I wanted to leave home and your father was available.'

'That's awful. Poor Dad.'

'Poor us. We both chose the wrong person.' The glare dissolved into a frown of determined fairness. 'But I'm not complaining. Dad treats me well, I've made my own life and we jog along together. We also have you.'

Their sole mutual accomplishment: an indulged teenager with plenty of confidence but no firm ideas about her future. I was firm with guys at parties, though. They soon gave up when I wouldn't let them give me love bites or get into my bra (defined as Second Base; Third Base was into your knickers, last stop on the steamy journey to All The Way). I hadn't been tempted to go beyond a brief snog – unlike Vron and Cuckoo who were already French-kissing.

'Yuck,' Jude said when they first told us. 'I wouldn't let anyone put his tongue in my mouth. Other people's spit smells.'

'But it feels nice. Squirmy.'

'Down *there,*' Vron confided in a husky whisper.

'That's disgusting.' Jude was only allowed to go to parties until ten when her aunt came to fetch her, and compensated by pooh-poohing the frolics that went on when the lights were turned down later.

'I agree.' Nobody had ever made me feel squirmy down *there.* Guys of our age were satyrs with raging pimples and sweaty hands. They didn't talk much, just grabbed. I longed to meet a debonair man of the world like – well, David Niven.

'You're both nuts,' they said to me and Jude, the first splinter in our solidarity. It brought the two of us closer together. After she turned sixteen and the dragon aunt had visited our home and quizzed Mum about proper supervision, Jude was allowed to stay with me sometimes. I'd offer to lend her things to wear to doll up her plain dresses for parties, though she always refused.

'I don't bloody care what I look like,' she'd say, turning her head away, though with her eyes lingering on the marcasite necklace or angora bunny jacket I was holding out.

'Go on, wear it, Jude. Your aunt won't see.'

She'd shrug, 'It's not because of *her*. I don't want to be conspicuous.'

'You won't. You'll fit in. Everybody's—

'I'm not everybody. Nor are you. We're thinkers, not party girls.'

Flattered as I was to be considered a thinker, I liked going to parties too. But the pull of solidarity was strong, and since Jude never wore make-up, I abandoned mascara and eye-shadow and cut down to a dab of lipstick. The idea of being above the common herd was new and exciting. We'd stand together assessing the boys at parties, commenting on their acne, clumsy dancing, ridiculous haircuts and the number of times they sidled outside with their partners. It earned us a reputation for being stuck up, which meant that only the brave asked us to dance.

'I don't bloody care,' she'd repeat after we got home and were lying awake in the dark talking about who was getting off with whom.

I pretended not to either, though secretly wished that Rory, the school cricket captain, would sometimes choose me. He could jive as though born to it, twirling his partners around with an expert guiding hand until their full-circle skirts flew out like frisbees. Jude's eyes followed him too, and it's the thing I remember best about her: the fact that her eyes revealed what she was really thinking.

She was homesick for her family and country, but I often wonder who she would have been without the strictures of her upbringing – so different from mine as an indulged only child. Would I have been someone else in another family? The nature versus nurture debate has cropped up often during my lifetime, and when I look at my very different twins who are so close, I can understand why there's never a conclusion.

The Fearsome Foursome drifted apart after school: Vron to a secretarial college in Joburg, Cuckoo to nurse at Addington, and Jude back to Uganda where – to general amazement – she joined a novitiate to become a nun.

'She never did like guys,' Vron said when she phoned to tell me the news, the last time I'd hear from her for eight years. 'If you don't want to get married, you either have to be a lesbian or a nun.'

We were so ignorant. All of us had what were then called maiden aunts whom we'd decided must be lesbians.

I protested, 'But she swore all the time. Nuns aren't supposed to swear.'

'They'll make her wear a chastity belt on her tongue.'

In the silence after we'd stopped giggling, I said, 'Maybe she wants to impress her Dad who runs that mission.'

'Maybe. See you, Annie.'

Vron's voice went all solemn and I wanted to bite my tongue; her father had died when she was a baby. Instead I said, 'Next hols, okay?'

'I'll probably have a job by then.'

Unusually for a fifties father, Dad agreed that I would benefit from going to university. The girls at school were lucky to get three months' secretarial training; many had to take jobs behind counters or sign on as hairdressing apprentices. Only the cleverest and luckiest got to university.

They drove me down with a set of matching suitcases, wearing a tweed suit with a nipped-in waist and a pencil skirt, my hair in a French pleat and carrying a patent leather handbag. Instant mortification! Everyone else was wearing slacks and sweaters and carrying rucksacks.

I squandered my first month's pocket money in one afternoon buying clothes to fit in, packed away the suit and Mum's carefully chosen accessories, and plunged into student life.

It was 1960 and the smug certainties of the fifties faded as the new decade began. The first shock of the year was Sharpeville, followed by the attempted assassination of Dr Verwoerd. Newspapers splashed the growing horror of thalidomide babies. Albert Luthuli was awarded the Nobel Peace Prize and John F Kennedy was president.

I'm ashamed to say that I hardly registered the increasing anguish of black resistance and police violence, even though Mum had joined the Black Sash and stood for hours with other women in silent demonstrations. She said it was the least she could do for the good woman who had worked for us for over twenty years, though when Mum got home with sore feet and a headache, she would call out as usual for her tray of tea.

But this story is about the politics between Doug and me and the difference careers made to our lives.

# 3

I soon learnt that university students were different from schoolboys only in one respect: they talked more than they grabbed. Talking was the college sport and winners were the ones who talked more bullshit than anyone else. As subjects for debate, the cold war and the horrors of living in the mushroom shadow of the H-bomb were waning in favour of the space race and the horrors of apartheid. The London Jive, wispy beards, corduroy and duffel coats were out; rock 'n' roll, sideburns and anoraks were in. People smoked Sobranie Black Russians to be sophisticated and there were occasional whiffs of dagga.

Doug Perceval was different – a serious law student who spent more time in the library than the Union. The campus buzz was that he didn't have time for a girlfriend because he was aiming for a Rhodes scholarship.

Way beyond my reach, I'd thought, and tried to concentrate on lectures and the innumerable essays demanded by English and History tutors. It was heady stuff, being called 'Miss' and asked for my opinions. School had been so dictatorial that it took time to form opinions – especially with tutors who preferred their own opinions gussied up and presented as the fruit of research and hard thought. The technique proved invaluable when I became a journalist.

The student body at our university was small enough for first-years to aspire to committees. I applied to join the dramatic society and the editorial team producing the Roneoed student newspaper, and should have realised when they snapped me up that eager beavers end up doing all the work.

Towards the end of September, everyone else deserted the newspaper to swot for exams and I became editor, sub-editor, layout person, proofreader and publisher of the final edition for the year. I was sweating over the layout table in the poky office when Doug Perceval knocked on the open door saying, 'Are you still taking ads for the final edition? I need to sell my bike.'

Mr Sandman of the song had sent me a dream. He could have stepped straight out of DH Lawrence in his rumpled shirt with the sleeves half rolled-up and baggy corduroys, his black hair falling in a wedge over eyes like dark blue slate. I stammered, 'Are you l-leaving varsity then?'

'Only next year. The Prof says I'm in line for a Rhodes if I keep up the hard work.' His small proud smile was quickly suppressed. 'So I've found digs just down the road and won't need a bike now.'

I thought, Play your cards right, girl, and said, 'Don't talk about hard work. I've been landed with the sub-editing *and* layout because all the others are swotting.'

He looked at me more closely then. 'Thought I recognised you. Stage manager for the Dram Soc's *Twelfth Night* in August, right?'

I nodded, gobsmacked with delight at being noticed. But he went on, 'My sympathies, babe. Arty types are experts at co-opting first years to do all the dirty work.'

Babe, he calls me! I parried with, 'Aren't you studying Law? That falls under Arts, so you're an arty type, too.'

'No way. Law is a hard slog. Latin must be the driest subject on earth.' He leant forward to confide, 'To be honest, I don't think I'm cut out to be a lawyer.'

Trying to stay calm in the close-up, I managed to breathe, 'What'll you do instead?'

'Aye, there's the rub. We did *Hamlet* in English I, in case you think I only study dead languages.' The small smile was back. 'Pa reckons I should see what's on offer when I've got my MA Oxon in the bag. He says the pick of the jobs go to guys with good qualifications who know how to work. Strivers, he calls them.'

'Strivers?'

'As in Tennyson's "Ulysses": "To strive, to seek, to find, and not to yield."' He struck a mock valiant pose with his fists raised. 'Pa admires Victorian virtues. I don't think he's even registered the dangers of the atomic age.'

At last! An intellectual discussion. I wanted it to go on and on. Existentialism had barely reached the colonies, though we had our share of black polo-necks huddled around tables where it was obligatory to smoke, arguing about ideas and liberal politics in wilful ignorance of the injustices outside our academic cocoon.

He went on, dropping his arms, 'But I'm getting off the point. I came to advertise my bike for sale. Is it too late?'

To keep him talking, I blurted, 'Haven't you got a brother to give the bike to?'

'No. There's just me.'

Snap. I said, 'Oh. I'm an only child too.'

His smile curved up at the ends then, followed by, 'What ho, Horatio! That's too good a coincidence to pass up. How about having coffee with me?'

'But I'm already late with the layout and—'

'Please?'

The smile prevailed over my feeble flicker of responsibility. I was a goner from the moment we chinked cups in the Students' Union.

That's where it all began. Soon we couldn't keep our hands off each other and confessed that we hadn't 'done it' with anyone else, but where my instinct was to hold back, his hormones fought epic battles with his honourable intentions. Before the term was over, we'd given in. He braved the chemist for a packet of FLs and I braved the student doctor for a Dutch cap. Just before sunset on a warm evening with miggies hovering, we ducked off the quiet path by the river, made a nest in the long grass with his jacket, and became lovers.

After rolling around hugging and kissing for a few minutes, his strained whisper crackled in my ear. 'Can we ...? Now?'

'Yes. Yes! I'm okay. I've put the thing in.' Slippery as a jellied eel, squirming like a live one as my inexpert fingers had wrestled and jabbed it into place.

'You get comfortable while—' He turned away, tearing at the packet with his teeth.

I wriggled my knickers off and tucked them under the jacket.

His hot face came down close to mine. 'Ready?'

'Yes.' I raised myself a bit to meet him. He straddled my thighs on his knees and felt for me with one trembling hand, guiding himself in with the other.

Invading. Burning.

There was no trace of the deep warm yielding feeling I had when we kissed and he fondled my body. I thought of Jude saying, 'Yuck. I wouldn't let anyone put his tongue in my mouth.' Yet I was letting Doug assault my most private place. This wasn't anything like …

And then he came with a great 'Ohhhhhh' of delight and relief, and it was over. We'd done it. He mumbled as he rolled away, 'I'll love you forever, Annie.'

Afterwards we lay whispering to each other, he with gratitude and me covering up my dismay. 'Making love' for the first time is so different from how you imagine it's going to be. Sex scenes in books and movies seem designed to make new lovers feel inadequate. There are no exploding rockets. No smoochy music. No soft-focus shadowy bodies coupling in ecstasy, he rhythmically rising and falling (controlled as a ballet dancer), she murmuring little moans on a rising note, as they ascend to magnificent mutual orgasms.

It took Doug and me a while to learn how to please each other. At the beginning he was always in a rush that left me behind. One day he grumbled that I was prudish and I flared, 'The hell I'm prudish! I let you do it, don't I?'

Bewildered, he protested, 'That's not what I want.'

'Could have fooled me.'

'I mean, I don't want you to *let* me do it. We're supposed

to be doing it together.' His frown looked as though someone had grooved it with a router.

'How? Nothing happens to me. You just – well, jump on and then it's all over.'

'Please don't be like that,' he begged. 'What do you want me to do? Tell me, Annie. I love you.' There were tears I'd never seen in his eyes.

'Go more slowly, then,' I said, mollified. And, 'Cuddle me first.' And, 'Kiss me for a longer time.' Until I start to feel squirmy down *there* went unsaid.

The handbooks available to lovers then were pathetic and *The Joy of Sex* was still a twinkle in Dr Alex Comfort's eye. But we learnt to tell each other what pleased and excited us and what made us feel uncomfortable. We became 'Doug and Annie', a committed couple in the throng of students intent on having a good time while they studied for some amorphous future.

Doug was good-looking rather than handsome, with a well-muscled body and the black hair of his Cornish ancestors. I loved the high flush on his cheekbones after squash or a run, and the feel of his warm skin under his shirts; I adored the way he tucked my arm under his as we walked and talked about our hopes and dreams. We confidently anticipated good jobs and a lovely home and children. We vowed undying loyalty to each other and planned an ideal family.

He was my safety net for twenty-nine years from that September day when the wild flowers in the grass where we first made love were like constellations of stars.

It was his mature sense of responsibility that made Doug

stand out from his contemporaries. He had goals where the rest were still wondering how to get through end-of-year exams. We were alike in many ways but quite different in others. I was gregarious where he was intense and industrious, burning to make a success of his life. His parents had emigrated with him from England after the war and his father had worked his way up in South African Railways from workshop apprentice to station master. As a self-educated man from a poor family, he had high ambitions for his bright only son and drove him accordingly.

'Pa taught me to aim for the top,' Doug told me once, 'and I seldom missed school. Ma supervised my endless homework, bringing tea and biscuits to fortify me while she told stories about her first job mending costumes for a theatre. When I was twelve I wanted to be an actor because it sounded exciting, and Pa nearly had a stroke. There were no more stories after that.'

His mother was a dressmaker, a tiny shy woman with needle-pricked fingers and the cautious smile of a wife who wasn't quite sure of herself in the presence of her talented men. They were so proud of Doug, yet oddly intimidated by his university education, which elevated him to a higher social class that wouldn't notice the railway houses they'd lived in. Even after we were married, I couldn't bring myself to call Mr Perceval 'Pa' like Doug did, though 'Ma' seemed just right for her.

After he'd graduated with honours as expected and won his Rhodes, he went off to Oxford while I soldiered on with my BA for another year, keeping my mind off the seductive appeal of his smile to other women by working as hard as I hoped he was. When I'd written my last exam, I walked out of the hall with jacaranda blossom crunching under my sandals and told Mum that I was going to join him.

She said, 'You can't,' and then, 'I thought you'd got over him.' His letters were addressed to the res.

'I'll never get over him. And if I don't go soon, someone else will snap him up. Doug is special.'

'Maybe someone already has?'

'If so, I'll beat her off. I'm going, Mum. I booked on the *Carnarvon Castle* two months ago and I've joined the Overseas Visitors' Club, so I'll have somewhere to stay.'

'This is a nasty shock. We've spoilt you,' she snapped. 'Too much pocket money.'

'Allowance, you mean. Which I've been saving like mad.'

'Not enough to live on without a job. And you've never had to fend for yourself. Do you even know how to cook?'

I had my answers ready. 'South African graduates qualify as supply teachers in England. I'll learn to cook.'

'You've got it all worked out, then. Sneaky child.'

'I'm not a child! I'm nearly twenty-one. We're lovers. I love him and he loves me.'

I braced myself for opposition but she only sighed, 'Ah, the old sweet dream. I should have seen this coming. All I can say is, be careful, darling. Don't make any rash decisions until you've got to know him better.'

This was unexpected. 'Does that mean you won't mind if we live together?'

'I can hardly stop you doing your own thing over there. Besides, I don't want you to make the mistake I made. Be sure you're right together before you commit yourself, Annie.' She had tears in her eyes. I remember them still.

Supply teaching meant London and I wanted to be with him, so I took a job on the *Oxford Mail* instead. After a second year of studying and with his MA pending, we decided that he should try for work in London – easy enough then for someone with English parents. He did the rounds of employers and was offered a position with a firm of property brokers based in the City. We rented a flat just off the Fulham Road, flew home Trek Airways via Khartoum and Lourenço Marques, and got married on my twenty-second birthday.

Our four-day honeymoon was spent flying back via Entebbe, Cairo and Malta, landing in the early afternoons and staying at grand hotels straight out of Agatha Christie. Our plan was for both of us to work for several years before having children so we could afford to buy a house when the time came. With my experience on the *Oxford Mail,* I'd managed to land a position as a junior reporter in a Fleet Street newsroom.

London was the centre of the world then, a dazzling forcefield magnetised by the Beatles and Carnaby Street. South African friends arrived to spend a few nights sleeping on our sagging sofa while they looked for jobs and their own digs, all of us dizzy with the exhilaration of working in a fabled city.

I saw a lot of Cuckoo, now a registered nursing sister doing a midwifery year at Queen Charlotte's. When we met again for the first time, I was startled by the brisk, serious person who came to meet me wearing a lace-edged cap and a diamante brooch with an upside-down watch pinned on her uniform. But away from the hospital, she was the old

Cuckoo who loved parties and smoked too much, always making others laugh, ricocheting from one boyfriend to another because she never found one who was just right. Like Doug, she said.

We had lost touch with Vron and never heard from Jude.

Doug's and my social life revolved around coffee bars with hissing espresso machines, cupboard-sized Chinese restaurants and bottle parties where we sat on floor cushions, drank plonk and dunked bread rolls in our soup. A special night out meant a convivial din of folk singers and guitars in the Troubador.

'We're so lucky,' we'd say to each other, toasting our socks in front of the gas fire.

He always qualified it with, 'Touch wood.'

He was the cautious one who weighed up the pros and cons before making decisions. I was more inclined to rush into things, yodelling enthusiasm. An oboe note of pessimism was part of his nature, as cheerfulness was part of mine. One of his guiding principles was, 'If you don't expect too much, you won't get disappointed.'

And I'd answer, 'Expectations make me happy.'

'Cock-eyed optimist.' He also grew up with the *South Pacific* songs.

'Not really. I want to enjoy things.'

'There's more to life.' The habitual frown gnarled his eyebrows. 'It's going to be hard work making our way here, Annie. Maybe we should go home.'

'One day. It's such fun in London.'

'Strivers aren't motivated by fun. We aim for goals.'

'Oh, don't be so stuffy!'

'I'm not. I'm a realist.' The glow of the gas fire highlighted one side of his face; the other side was in shadow. 'Life's been easy for you. I've had to work damn hard to get here from the railway houses Pa qualifies for.'

I took his hand between both of mine. 'Heavy weather warning.'

'One of us has to keep watch for storms.'

'Hurricanes too?' I teased, trying to lighten his mood.

'As long as they blow us in the right direction.'

We had no reason to doubt that they would. Doug had been chosen for a management training programme which included courses in property law and foreign exchange at the London School of Economics. I was thriving on my new job – even scoring the occasional byline. When the time came, we would go home well equipped for possible careers.

'I'll be able to walk into a top job there with my qualifications,' he'd say.

'What about me?'

'You'll bring up our family, then work on a newspaper when they're old enough. We could buy a house with a swimming pool in a good suburb …'

Doug's worrying aside, neither of us doubted our life's path or its rosy prospects.

Among our wedding presents were four wooden salad bowls, a Denbyware dinner service, an electric waffle iron, a hideous cut glass vase and (from my parents) a canteen of sleek stainless steel cutlery. Chosen by us, of course; Mum had wanted to give silver. She wrote to say that she was going to painting classes now that I was safely off the shelf, but that she and Dad were missing me. Not missing them at all, I wrote home dutifully when I had time.

It was the mid-sixties, miniskirts and Mary Quant were shocking the oldies, and we were surfin' into our new life along with the Beach Boys, confident of the future.

# 4

After stately Oxford, working on a London newspaper was like driving on an express motorway. I learnt to be a big-city journalist through trial and error, blood, sweat and tears, aided by the pickety-pockety-pickety-pock of an Underwood typewriter.

I was taught to write fast, punchy reports with a maximum of two short sentences per paragraph, though they never got past the chief sub-editor unscathed. He was a peevish perfectionist who couldn't keep his red pencil off clean copy – even the columnists' near-sacred prose. But the highs of dramatic events and breaking scandals carried me through the tedium of market prices and magistrates' courts. And I made two good friends.

Ginger and Susie sat on either side of me and we'd scurry out for sandwiches at lunchtime and find a bench in the Inner Temple gardens to gossip over them. Ginger had started with me at the very bottom, where junior reporters lurked like pond life: she had long pale goldfish hair and a pearly skin and the temperament of a piranha in pursuit of a story. Susie, whose comely plumpness disguised a cynical wit and whose mother was a Lady, had joined the paper a year earlier as a social reporter and regaled us with stories of the rich at play. In the hectic clatter of the newsroom we vied for bylines, hoarded contacts in little black books and slaved over our copy. I was able to put in a lot of useful overtime while Doug did his courses in preparation for the executive ladder.

By the time our first baby was due three years later, Susie had left to marry Xavier, a Dutch architect, and work in his practice, Ginger had been poached by the *Daily Telegraph* and I had been elevated to assistant editor on the women's pages. It was hard to leave the paper's congenial buzz, though I'd bought the typewriter and had negotiated with my editor Lally Woodkiss to continue working from the flat as a freelancer. My married friends and I were resigned to stay-at-home motherhood. Those were early days for The Pill, and the unmarried ones had not yet attained the nirvana of sex without consequences which made us so envious later.

My labour was long and painful despite the laughing gas, though the end result was worth the anguish: an eight-pound boy who had Doug's black hair, slate-blue eyes and a quizzical frown when he was puzzled by an odd sound. Robin was an amiable baby who ate and slept well and played with his cot toys when he woke up, so I was able to work for several hours every day.

Lally phoned me four months after he was born to tell me that she was now editing a monthly magazine called *Modern Lifestyle*. 'Brand new and flying off the shelves already,' she boasted. 'My magic touch, of course. You want to be involved?'

'In what way?' Caution was the operative mode when Lally demanded anything. We'd called her The Ballbreaker in the newsroom.

'I need a cooking feature for my readers. Thought you'd be interested.'

'Me? You're joking. We had a maid who did most of the cooking while I was growing up.'

She snorted. 'You colonials. I suppose your mother sits around ordering the servants about.'

'Don't be insulting. Mum's Black Sash and does charity work.'

'Bully for her. But it's you I'm after. You must have learnt to make meals by now.'

'Well, yes. Out of books, mainly.'

'Supper for the slaving breadwinner? Pot luck for visitors?'

'Of course.'

'Plus, you've got a bit of style and you're good at research. I recall an excellent piece about career choices.'

'Thanks, but I don't see where this is—'

'And you can write, that's number one. Think "fabulous fast food". I want meals that are quick to prepare and inexpensive, but also classy. Low cash, plenty of dash. Lazy Sunday lunches, pot-luck suppers for friends. Tea and cakes for visiting relatives. Birthday feasts for kids and how to tempt reluctant eaters – you know, stuff like banana and raisin faces on the custard.'

'Ah.' The petty concerns of housewives weren't on my radar. I'd sent out feelers to various publications representing myself as an investigative journalist focused on the problems of working women.

'What do you mean, "ah"?'

'Serious topics are my thing. You know that.'

'I'm not looking for haute cuisine,' she scoffed. 'I want a young homemaker with original ideas. I want my WAM to feel confident she can put on stylish meals for next to nothing.'

'WAM?'

'Wife and mother. Target readership. Women at home feel they're missing out these days. They've gone off knitting and sewing and want to read about new ways of cooking and decorating. That's where my mag comes in.'

I tried again. 'Honestly, I'm more interested in women's issues: inadequate training, unequal pay, how to prevent another thalidomide disaster. Can't you give me a more meaty assignment?'

There was a sardonic chuckle. 'You can use as much meat as you like. We'll pay reasonable costs.'

'Don't patronise me!'

'I'm not. I'm offering you a year's contract for a substantial column that you can research and write at home. Steady work, darling.'

'But it's – well, it's a comedown after the newsroom.'

She went tsk-tsk-tsk and growled, 'Let me get this straight. You won't consider my offer because you'd feel demeaned by writing about food for fifty thousand readers?'

'I didn't say that. I said—'

'We pay well and you're not in a position to be choosy. I'll give you till four this afternoon to make up your mind,' and slammed the receiver down.

I had been working on two spec articles which I'd hoped to place with the newspaper because our bank account was in starvation mode after buying all the stuff a new baby was supposed to need then. Layettes included a shawl, six viyella nighties, six vests, six bibs, a dozen Harrington gauze squares and two dozen terrycloth nappies. We'd also invested in a crib, a cot, a high chair, a playpen and pram, all second-hand. The pram was a cream-and-gold carriage on elevated springs which got sideways looks in the Fulham Road and took ten minutes to manhandle up the stairs to the flat.

The thing is, I was used to earning my own money at a time when most of my friends were getting a weekly 'housekeeping allowance' from their husbands. Doug and I were a modern couple who believed in equality and mutual respect, and that our roles in the marriage weren't set in concrete. He could fry steaks and bake potatoes if I was too busy to cook, and I'd put plugs on new appliances and change light bulbs and empty the rubbish bin – all then the domain of the Man of the House.

Being independent and able to maintain my side of the bargain was important, so I had only a brief wrangle with my pride before phoning Lally back and accepting the commission.

'Great,' she said, all snippy so I'd know my doubts had displeased her. 'I'll expect your first piece on Monday week: a thousand words including recipes. The theme is a three-course dinner for six costing not more than ten bob a head, wine included. I'm not talking caviar and Château Margaux, right?'

'Less than three pounds for the lot!'

'That's the most we'll pay. Think something cool and chic to start with: a pretty little salad in a lettuce leaf? Think a main course French casserole – coq au vin? – so you can use the cheaper cuts of meat. And make a nursery pudding for dessert. Englishmen equate jam roly-poly with love, poor fools.'

I quavered, 'All I can do is try.'

'Try, hell. You come up with the goods or else, darling. I need panache above and beyond *Good Housekeeping*. I'll make you the British homemaker of the year if you pull finger.'

Just what I'd always wanted to be. 'Thanks very much.'

Without a trace of irony she said, 'Don't mensh. Glad to help out. Let me know in good time what night you'll be doing the dinner so I can send my photographer round. Deadline's Monday week, remember?' The receiver clattered down again.

Doug was enthusiastic. 'It's a great start, Annie. A regular income will mean you can spend more time on your investigative articles. Plus, we get a free meal once a month.'

'Free ingredients. Hard work for me, though.'

'And me. I'll help when I don't have other commitments.'

Of course. He sometimes worked late and still played squash to keep fit. He also changed nappies and bathed Robin if he got home early enough – a model father. And lover. Practice was making perfect.

We invited Susie and Xavier van Breda and Cuckoo and her current boyfriend to dinner, and I began to think about a menu.

Convenience food was limited to fish and chips and hot dogs then – no pizzas or popping into a delicatessen for smoked trout fillets or dolmades. Margarine and whipped evaporated milk were substitutes for the lavish pre-war butter and cream. Even post–Elizabeth David, garlic was treated with caution. One of my cookbooks warned: 'To impart a subtle flavour of garlic, it is usually sufficient to cut a single clove and rub it round the side of the salad bowl. Unless you are sure that everyone who will be eating the salad is fond of garlic, it is best to omit this very distinctive flavouring.'

So it was a demanding challenge to conjure up innovative meals with flair that were also inexpensive, quick and easy for busy women to make. I had no sense of being one of the pioneers of the revolution in cooking habits. Lally had put me to the test and I was damn well going to show her I could do it, to disprove one of the prevailing myths: a good mind needn't go as limp as boiled cabbage after the onset of motherhood.

I consulted my shoebox of cut-out recipes, two cookbooks inherited from Mum and a more eclectic pile from the library before settling on: salmon mousse (tinned salmon in a mixture of home-made mayonnaise, yoghurt, cream, chopped dill, gelatine and seasoning, set in a mould, then turned out and served with lemon slices and toast triangles); beef stroganoff (an economy recipe lifted from an advertisement for Campbell's soup in an old American magazine, using slivered stewing steak in place of fillet, simmered in tinned beef consommé until tender, mushrooms and evaporated milk soured with lemon juice and thickened with cornflour, served on ribbon noodles); and treacle tart with a lattice crust and whipped cream.

The ingredients cost two pounds fifteen shillings, with a little help from my grocery cupboard. Doug chose a vin ordinaire to go with the main course and the Van Bredas brought a bottle too. Susie came early to help me lay out the meal for the photographer on our red gingham tablecloth on the kitchen table, set off by nasturtiums in a silver sugar bowl.

The photographer, Zeke Joszefs, admired the spread with such longing in his voice that we asked him to stay and eat with us, making jokes about loaves and fishes as we grew tipsy on the unaccustomed wine. He went on taking photos and the fun showed in laughing candlelit faces and ruby wine glowing in the cheap glasses that were all we could afford. It was a wonderful evening and Doug said when everyone had gone and we were washing dishes and clearing up, 'That was great, Annie. You're a marvel.'

'Do you really think so?' It had been hard work.

'Yes, I do.' He put his dripping hands on my shoulders and drew me into the warm haven of his arms. 'You're a marvel and I love you.'

'I love you too. And you're pretty good yourself, oh brave climber of the executive ladder.' I snuggled against him and felt his heart beating under his ribs, strong and sure.

'It's not what I'd thought it would be,' he mumbled into my ear.

'What isn't?'

'The job. It's more hard slog than brain work.'

'Bosses like to extract their pound of flesh,' I said, trying to sound as though I knew all about these things. Executive wives were supposed to be staunch and supportive, always there for their men.

'Only it feels like a ton.'

'Never mind, darling. You're on the way up, that's the main thing.'

I was so ignorant. So unaware of his struggles.

The meal was a wow with Lally and her readers, who responded with an avalanche of mail begging for more. It was the heyday of the bright new women's magazine that ran articles about current issues and trends and used spectacular photographs that bled off the page, eclipsing the stodgy old formula of knitting patterns, family recipes, stiffly posed fashion and romantic short stories. And more the readers got, month after month, illustrated in succulent full colour. Lally whipped up the response at first by forging enthusiastic letters to the editor, making her readers feel that they were demanding the articles she was delighted to supply – amply funded by the advertising they generated.

Thanks to her manipulations and Zeke's luscious photographs, my *Fabulous Fast Food* columns became one of the hits of the late sixties and seventies, devoured by homemakers as far afield as Vancouver, Hong Kong, Dar-es-Salaam and New Zealand. It was a huge boost for my ego which would otherwise have been mired in a succession of household chores and nappies, turning out the occasional thoughtful article on spec.

I didn't use my own name on the columns. Lally said 'Anne Perceval' sounded too stuck-up for a popular magazine, and anyway I didn't want former Fleet Street colleagues to know that I'd stooped to writing domestic trivia. The byline on the columns, dreamt up by the publisher's advertising agency, was 'Annie Butterfield'. I thought it sounded twee, but Lally said it was just right for *Modern Lifestyle* – 'warm and natural'. The column logo was a blue and white Cornishware jug of field poppies and graceful grass-heads.

During this time Doug was given his first promotion, as office liaison manager for the Midlands property division, which meant that he did a lot of travelling. There were compensations: a higher salary and a subsistence allowance, plus several nights a week when I could work late without impinging on our time together. When he came home at the weekend I'd organise a babysitter for the evening and we'd go out on a date, then go home and make love until we fell asleep.

It was all a game then. We didn't worry about contraception, having decided on a family. The babies would come along in due course.

After three years we could afford to move up the housing scale and rent a semi-detached with a back garden in Chiswick. By then we needed more space for Robin and the coming new baby – a girl, we hoped. Amply fulfilled by our deepening relationship, our eager little son and interesting work that kept us involved and busy, we scaled down the idea of a family. Woodstock and Joan Baez and feminism had changed our generation's horizons. Children were no longer the main reason for getting married but components of the good life we expected to lead in one of the world's great cities. Things were working out so well for us that the idea of going home to South Africa to live and work had begun to fade. We were Londoners now.

In those pre-scan days, it was a major shock to be told four months into the pregnancy that there were two babies on the way. Mum had never thought to mention that Granny's sister, who had emigrated to Canada after World War I, had specialised in twins.

# 5

Robin was three when the twins were born, grown from a phlegmatic baby into a dynamo who charged about vrooming cars and kicking balls and throwing things out of the windows, chuckling at our bleats of 'Naughty boy!' The flowerbed under his bedroom had to be relieved daily of its burden of toys, socks, shoes, pyjamas, apple cores, bread crusts, mugs and (his favourite) keys. As he grew older, he threw further. Soon most of the keys in the house had been swallowed by undergrowth and our char Ivy complained that she couldn't lock the lavatory door when she needed 'a bit of privacy, like'. Doug and I spent a whole afternoon doing a round-up with rakes, then attaching jazzy plastic tags to each key so they would be easier to find.

Robin's other talent was asking questions; 'Why?' and 'How?' were a constant chorus. He was a sturdy little boy with Doug's athletic reflexes and engaging smile. At times he also exhibited his father's anxiety to do well – whether it was innate or learnt I could never decide. He wanted to kick balls higher and further than other children, to run faster and shout louder. If anyone beat him, he sulked and refused to go on playing. The frown lines between his eyebrows deepened while he waited for answers to his questions.

'He's going to be an ace cross-examiner,' Doug would say. 'We'd better put his name down for the Middle Temple now.'

Though Doug had eaten his dinners and been admitted to the English Bar, he had not joined the legal department in the property firm, saying, 'I'm on the executive path. Why get tied up in technicalities?'

He played the part to the hilt: wore discreet dark suits and silk ties, spoke well and to the point, worked long hours, stroked his boss's ego, and always stood his share of rounds in the pub – though his colleagues were less than friendly. When I met them at company events, each one told me what a good chap he was, so serious and determined. I didn't realise that they were belittling him. It wasn't common knowledge then that good chaps, however serious and determined, didn't go places. It was the impatient bastards with fire in their bellies who were more likely to reach the top.

Being too serious was probably why he hadn't made even a half-blue for cross-country at Oxford: it was the daredevil runners who shone.

Unaware of these deficiencies, he soldiered on at work and I was happy in our new home. Robin went off to a play group every morning and Ivy did the housework, giving me plenty of time to organise and write my columns and research my articles.

I wrote the October-deadline column a week before the twins' birth. Lally had requested a Sunday luncheon for twelve costing no more than ten pounds. Ivy came in for the morning as a special favour, 'Seeing as you're about to pop.'

It was a major concession for a bingo addict who arrived yawning every weekday at about nine, filled the washing machine, had a cup of tea, pulled up the bedclothes, mopped the bathroom, had a cup of tea, did some light dusting and tidying, had a cup of tea, filled the tumble dryer, emptied the dishwasher, had a cup of tea, folded the washing, ironed the few items that weren't drip-dry, had a cup of tea and went home, still yawning.

She stayed awake long enough that morning to polish the silver tray inherited from Granny, lay the table and do all the cutting and chopping. While Doug cooked, I sat on a stool and did the arranging. The twins were doing vigorous aquabatics and my feet were killing me.

We'd invited five of his colleagues and their partners, hoping to impress them. How naïve it was to think we could impress sophisticated London property brokers and their womenfolk (that's what one of them had said when Doug invited him: 'May we bring our womenfolk, old man?') with my inexpensive meal and a family home with toy boxes shoved behind the sofa. They perked up when Zeke arrived to take the magazine photographs, posing for him with raised glasses and party smiles.

Thanks to the two salmon provided by a helpful friend of Doug's (Lally's costing rules allowed gifts of food in season), there were three bottles of Mateus Rosé to go with the meal: an assortment of canapés on the silver tray, garnished with chive and fennel flowers; poached salmon served with homemade mayonnaise, potatoes dauphinoise and a green salad;

and vanilla ice cream with hot chocolate sauce. I'd made the ice cream the day before, and Zeke's elegant photograph of snowy peaks capped with melted chocolate and wreathed in scarlet rosehips later won an award.

At the end of the meal our guests murmured, 'Jolly good,' and 'Not too bad at all, this Portuguese rosé,' and Doug made a little speech saying he was proud to have such an accomplished wife.

'So pregnant too.' The boss's personal assistant Nerine was chic, willowy, twenty-eight and still single.

'They're due next week.' I patted my enormous bulge, trying to look modest and telling myself she was on the shelf.

'How lovely.' She produced the faint smile she used on everyone below the level of senior executive.

'Our doctor's given me permission to be present, as long as I wear operation scrubs and a mask,' Doug boasted. It was a new thing, allowing husbands in the delivery room. Only the most progressive maternity hospitals indulged what most doctors believed to be a ridiculous idea.

'Brave chap,' Nerine murmured.

Deceived by the illusion that we had our lives under control, we weren't prepared for mayhem when Tasha came screaming into the world, followed by Chloe who had to be held upside down and smacked before she consented to yell.

They arrived in a hurry the following Sunday. We called the ambulance and went howling into Queen Charlotte's, having left Robin with a neighbour. Doug went green and fainted minutes into the final stage of labour, missing both births. He only came round after the babies had been washed and swaddled in receiving blankets and nestled in my weary arms. Tasha was still yelling, a tomato face under a bristle of dark hair. Chloe gave him a flinty glare that included Cuckoo, who had pulled strings to be with me for the delivery. She'd helped him to his feet hissing, 'Get up, Daddy. Your daughters need you.'

It was a prescient comment. Those two were hell on wheels: colic, screaming, projectile vomiting, hot mustard nappies, the lot. Ivy was no help with small babies beyond warming up their bottles, and Mum wasn't available even when I begged on the phone. Her excuse was, 'Sorry, darling, there are two charity dinners coming up and I've booked for a painting course.' So Doug had to take his annual two weeks' leave early. We worked in shifts: one on duty while the other collapsed into oblivion. More than once I woke on my back with a twin gobbling at each tit, Doug having rolled me over and propped them on pillows and guided each ravenous little mouth onto its target.

He was a pillar of strength throughout the ordeal, keeping Robin occupied and doing the other chores refused by Ivy, which included visits to the laundrette with bagfuls of reeking nappies. For years he told hilarious stories about how he had crouched in front of the washing machines to conceal the smelly horrors as he stuffed them into the drums under the basilisk gazes of little old ladies come to wash their smalls. Disposable nappies were a distant dream then.

Nobody knows exhaustion until they have struggled through the first month of raising twins – or at the very least, crossed the Antarctic alone on foot. Sleep deprivation doesn't begin to describe the profound bone-weariness of demand-feeding two vociferous little bundles at different times. The girls had inherited their father's determination: they were so intent on draining me to the last drop that they glugged down more than their tiny tummies could handle, which meant vomiting it all up again and an even hungrier assault on my quailing nipples at the next feed.

I wept for hours when Doug had to go back to work, wondering why we hadn't gone home, where a nanny would have been available and nappies could dry in the sun.

# 6

In a final burst of helpfulness before Doug went back to the daily grind, he dreamt up the idea for my February column: a Valentine's Day dinner for two which could be prepared and cooked within half an hour by a boyfriend who wanted to set a romantic scene for a proposal. We decided on the menu together. Lally's brief was that the cost of ingredients (including flowers and wine) should be under four pounds and, for authenticity's sake, Doug should do both the shopping and the cooking.

'He'd have to do it anyway,' I moaned. 'I'm totally housebound at the moment. You wouldn't believe how demanding the twins are.'

Her answer snapped back like a stretched elastic band. 'On the contrary, I know damn well. Why do you think I haven't had kids? I'm a twin myself. We drove our parents crazy.' Which explained a lot. Lally remains the most impossible woman I have ever met.

The twins were (for once) both asleep when Zeke arrived on Saturday morning to take photographs. He was a big friendly

Hungarian with wild hair like iron filings and the brawny hands of a lumberjack. Yet those huge fingers caressed his battery of cameras with infinite grace, and he had an eye for detail that exalted the humblest meal into a feast. Zeke's beautiful photographs were vital to the success of *Fabulous Fast Foods*. He also gave us an invaluable gift by taking regular photographs of the kids, 'To finish up the spool,' he'd say to Lally. But to me he said he loved the light on children's faces. Only years later when he held an exhibition of children's portraits did we discover that he had lost his wife and baby daughter in Bergen-Belsen.

Doug threw himself into his Valentine's Day meal with gusto. Having lined up all the implements and ingredients he needed, he started the oven timer and whizzed round the kitchen, scrubbing new potatoes and baby carrots and putting them on to boil in separate pots, laying the small round table by the window with a lace cloth, silver, red candles and a bowl with three floating red roses, sculpting herb-flavoured cottage cheese into two heart shapes ringed with cucumber slices, olives and melba toast, frying two fillet steaks in butter, boiling frozen peas with fresh mint (Lally allowed frozen vegetables), then arranging the main course on two plates with a blob of creamed horseradish on each steak.

All this took just twenty-nine minutes and Doug was so chuffed that he gloated, 'Eureka! Chalk one up for men in the kitchen.'

Zeke had set up his tripod so the loaded plates were against a dark background that highlighted the rich colours and rising steam. When he'd finished clicking, he said, 'I hate to be a spoilsport, but there's no dessert. Lally wants dessert too.'

'Fear not. It's under control.' Doug whipped away the plates and replaced them with flutes of pink champagne, into one of which went my engagement ring, fizzing prettily as it sank. 'Voilà! The pièce de résistance. Romantic or what?'

The three of us demolished the meal and were knocking back the last of the champagne when the twins woke and started caterwauling. Zeke rushed into the bedroom, snapped off the last of his film as fast as he could, then fled. He called that portrait 'Double Trouble'.

At the foot of the Valentine column I credited 'My very special husband, who prepared the meal'. Couples wrote in to *Modern Lifestyle* from all over the world thanking us for suggesting a memorable way to make a proposal, though there were a few complaints from girlfriends who had disliked their beloveds' choice of ring. 'And the jeweller wouldn't take it back because it was all sticky!' one indignant letter ended.

Lally was pleased. 'We've had amazing reader response. Keep it up.'

'The Valentine meal was all Doug's doing.'

'That was the point. A romantic repast made by a bachelor.'

'He helped me with the next three columns too,' I admitted. We'd done a birthday party with a clown theme for Robin, a dinner for four made in a pressure cooker, and a christening high tea in honour of the twins.

'I'm not complaining.'

'But we can't go on like this!' I wailed. 'He's on a new course with a horrendous workload, exhausted when he gets home. And I can't think straight any more, let alone plan innovative meals.'

‘Get more help, kiddo,’ she said in the crisp what-the-hell-are-you-moaning-about tone she used on her staff.

‘Where from?’ A pathetic response that showed how feeble I had become – verging on limp boiled cabbage.

‘You grew up with servants, for god’s sake. Phone an au pair agency. I’ll double what we pay for the column. You’re worth it. Circulation’s up by twenty per cent.’ The receiver crashed down before I could thank her. Lally believed in terse conversations. Her time was too valuable to put up with trivia, she said.

Doug was delighted. ‘Well done! You get time off to write and I get my wife back.’

‘The problem is to find someone who can put up with the racket.’ The twins spent most of their waking moments testing new decibel levels, and poor little Robin had to whine loud and long for attention.

‘Ask for previous experience with difficult babies.’

There is a knack to saying things that are obvious; he could be quite irritating in his rational mode. I said, ‘S’pose you’re right,’ trying not to sound ungracious. He was a paragon compared with most husbands then, who did their own thing regardless. Doug did his best to please everyone, from his boss down to Robin. He’d been showing signs of strain since the twins arrived, though, and I was at the end of my tether: an all-day slag in my candlewick dressing gown, the only garment that gave instant access to both milk bars when the twins demanded feeding.

The au pair agency waved a wand and Yselle Citron came into our lives: a sparky French nurse aide who had worked in an orphanage before coming to London to improve her English. The babies attached themselves to her at once. They didn't stop yelling, just transferred their demands from me to this new person who didn't get tetchy. Robin loved her too because she made him paper water bombs and fried eggy-bread with cinnamon sugar.

Yselle was built like a bull terrier with the muscular legs and deep tan of someone who had always walked everywhere; she came from a village in the Pyrenees. Her dark cropped curls and balsamic-brown eyes were complemented by a calm temperament and firm ideas about child-rearing that gave her the domestic authority I lacked, always happier at my typewriter than when wiping bums and snotty noses.

There was just one problem: Ivy. Yselle was scandalised by her sloppiness and inefficiency and wanted me to fire her, but I didn't have the heart, and anyway liked her humming as she worked.

'Okay, zen I fix 'er,' Yselle announced.

'How? She takes offence if I tell her what to do.' I'd tried at the beginning of her tenure, with little effect. Ivy went her own way and got enough drudgery done to justify her expense.

An electric grin exposed the gap between Yselle's upper front teeth, a feature Robin admired for its ability to emit piercing wolf whistles. 'You are too going-easy, Madame Anne,' she said. 'I fix Ivy, okay?'

Yselle had Ivy licked into shape within weeks, having convinced her that Frenchwomen are born beauty experts. First there was a new gamine haircut, then a fetching candy-striped overall, and soon a shared mid-morning tisane instead of the sugary tea that had given Ivy hips like a Roman urn. They dwindled visibly as she began to follow the 'housework fitness routine' Yselle prescribed as a sure route to glowing health and a sexy body. Unlike me, she'd managed to winkle out the reason why Ivy was so lackadaisical: following a bitter divorce, she had given up on men and begun to decline into disconsolate middle age.

To quote Perdita in *The Winter's Tale,* 'Sure this robe of mine / Doth change my disposition.' Aided by our record player, a carousel began to twirl round the house. The vacuum cleaner purred to the music of French accordions until there wasn't a speck of dust to be seen. The toys that had once lain underfoot for days were magicked away to the dreamy crooning of Johnny Hallyday and Sacha Distel. The iron whistled back and forth as she hummed 'Frère Jacques' and 'Alouette, gentille alouette'. Pretty soon, a man was waiting at the gate when Ivy left for home, beaming instead of yawning.

'Et voilà, Madame Anne,' Yselle said with a flourish of eloquent fingers the first time he appeared. 'I fix 'er! And she 'appy, eh?'

'She's happy and Doug's happy and I'm happy,' I said, crossing my fingers as I wished with all my heart that Yselle would stay forever – or at least until the twins were old enough to go away to college.

But of course she couldn't. Two years of periodic tranquillity was what she gave us, by which time the twins were trotting off with Robin to the play group on weekday mornings and relative peace descended.

In Vietnam the last American troops were leaving. In

Uganda Jude had been posted to the Kumi Leprosy Settlement where she taught in the primary school for little patients and the children of lepers. She wrote rare airmail letters that Cuckoo and I shared, equally impressed by her commitment and her funny stories about the difficulties faced by kids without fingers.

'They're well looked after here and I feel at home and needed,' she wrote once. 'So you needn't worry about me pitching up on your doorsteps one day ringing a bell, in case I'm contaminated. It's the least infectious of diseases. I'd have to French-kiss lepers all day to catch it.'

Apart from these and Mum's letters and brief long-distance phone calls on birthdays, our South African lives seemed like the distant past. Though Mum sometimes hinted that Doug could walk into a corporate position and I'd have a much easier life, we no longer discussed the idea of going home one day.

# 7

My *Fabulous Fast Food* columns had become one of the most popular features in *Modern Lifestyle.* Readers liked the formula of imaginative, inexpensive, easy meals served in real homes and gardens. I begged and borrowed ideas, recipes, ingredients, props and friends' houses as venues.

Ginger had become an arts editor known for her theatrical feuds, crossing swords often with Kenneth Tynan. She lived near Hammersmith Bridge in a beautiful flat overlooking the river, which I used a number of times. Her collection of antique embroidered silk shawls hung on the walls like giant butterflies. Zeke fell in love with her over a Hungarian goulash he had offered to cook for an informal supper feature, and moved in a week later. Willowy Ginger with her sleek goldfish hair and the grizzly bear of a photographer were nicknamed Beauty and the Beast by gossip columnists. I was delighted for Zeke because he had been lonely for so long.

Susie van Breda was interested in cooking and often came to help me, then carried her share of the free meal home to Xavier who was always hungry. Long before Martha Stewart was heard of, we covered the social spectrum from informal weddings, christening teas and kids' birthdays to cocktail parties and dinners, country breakfasts to bonfire nights.

Once, with Dad in mind, I put together a picnic for a fisherman's wife to take down to the riverbank and surprise her old man – perhaps even divert him from his angler's daydream for an hour or so.

When I asked Mum during a long-distance call if she'd seen it, she laughed and said, 'You're farting against thunder, darling. Fishermen don't go in for fancy food. They sit there vacantly gnawing on doorstep sandwiches.'

'Dad catches trout for you, doesn't he?'

'Not for *me*. For himself. He's in relentless competition with his cronies about weights and sizes, then wants me to cook the damn things as well. Trout is grossly overrated.'

I said, 'Doug's colleagues loved the poached salmon I did.'

It earned me a sardonic chuckle. 'I'm still struggling to come to terms with your career as a domestic goddess. You never did a hand's turn at home.'

'You didn't do the housework either.'

'But I looked after you and Dad and ran the house and volunteered for charities. I must have been mad. Should've done my own thing years ago.'

'What do you mean, your own thing?'

'Oh, this and that,' she said airily.

'Another charity?' I persisted.

'You *are* being quizzy today.'

'And you're not answering my questions.'

She took a while to answer, as if considering whether to

admit to a secret vice, then said, 'I need some privacy, smarty-pants.'

'But I want to know,' I whined, regressing at least twenty years. It wasn't like Mum to be evasive. She'd been playing hard to get for quite a while, I realised. Apart from a flying visit to meet the twins and sending presents for Christmas and birthdays, she hadn't been the doting grandmother I'd expected. 'What are you up to?'

'Painting classes. I told you.'

'Oh, those.' I was relieved. I'd thought she might have got herself involved with one of those earnest movements like goat-hair spinning, or fulminating against apartheid outside the Union Buildings in Pretoria. Mum was a dedicated member of the Black Sash and wrote furious letters to the newspapers when she felt strongly about something.

'*Life*-painting,' she said, sounding annoyed. 'I'm serious, not just dabbling with pretty watercolours. My art teacher says I have real talent. We're working towards a group exhibition.'

'Life-painting? You mean ...?'

'Oh, yes. Naked men. Young, gorgeous, well-hung naked men in languorous poses. Three times a week. In oils.'

'Mum! You can't be.' I hadn't thought she knew what well-hung meant.

'Why not? I'm painting them, not bedding them. Get real, dear.'

Good grief. I moaned, 'What does Dad say?'

'Guess.'

That wasn't difficult. Dad growled, 'Give me a decent bloody bite from a trout any day,' to most of the things other people said they liked.

She went on, 'I've discovered that I'm a damn good painter. Pity it took so long to find out. When I think of all the sumptuous bodies I could have immortalised instead of fundraising and running after you.'

'You don't mean that.'

'I *do*. I've wasted far too much of my time and energy on others. Now I'm doing something for me. Royal Academy, here I come.'

'That's great,' I said, not meaning it. Mothers should be available when you need them, not consorting with gorgeous, naked, well-hung young men.

I always forget that she's been listening to the tone of my voice for years. She murmured, 'Nothing wrong with ambition, Annie. You used to say you wanted to make your mark with serious articles but now it's all women's magaziney stuff. Hardly deathless prose.'

Touché. I'd been preening myself over my career and she was tired of being condescended to. But I couldn't help bursting out, 'It's not just women's magaziney stuff! It's lifestyle journalism. I've got the biggest readership of any Commonwealth cookery writer. And you know I also write serious articles.'

She surprised me with a belly laugh. 'There's no need to be defensive. I boast about you to my friends. Just give me some credit too, okay?'

Sharp as a tack, Dad always used to say of her. Not wanting to expose myself to more jabs below the belt, I mumbled, 'Okay.'

One of the reasons the *Fabulous Fast Food* concept became such a success was that it coincided with the fading importance of the dinner party and the move to more relaxed entertaining. Mum had abandoned her hostess role and was feeding Dad on fish 'n' chips and hamburgers picked up on the way home from art classes. Much to his delight, I'm sure.

Lally had increased my space to two double-page spreads glowing with Zeke's photographs, and my pay rose accordingly. Thanks to Yselle's astute management of the household and the kids on weekdays, I had more time and began to work on a collection of my best columns for a *Fabulous Fast Food* cookbook. This was several years before Fontana published the cheerful series by Ursel and Derek Norman (*Use Your Loaf*, *Salad Days*, *Soup Beautiful Soup*) and a good decade before the emergence of coffee table cookbooks lavishly illustrated in full-page colour. Lally said it wasn't a bad idea but she'd have to see a detailed proposal and sample layouts before she'd commit to it. Galvanised, I dreamt of being an actual Author instead of a mere cookery columnist.

There was good news for Doug as well: after two-and-a-half years of travelling back and forth to the Midlands coalface, he had been promoted to assistant manager of the London Counties property division.

'I won't have to sit on trains any more,' he told me as we clinked glasses to celebrate. 'And I'm aiming for the boss's job. He's only a short way off retirement. How would you like to be married to the manager of London Counties?'

'Very, *very* much.' I hugged him, loving the yeasty warmth

of his body when he was pumped up and ebullient. 'You deserve it.'

But he pulled back, frowning. 'Damn, I shouldn't have said that. We mustn't count our chickens.'

Echoing Mum, I said, 'Nothing wrong with ambition, Doug. It's okay to dream.'

'Tempting fate, though.'

'Rubbish. You're a striver, remember? Think positive. You'll be able to get stuck into the new job without wasting time travelling.'

'You sound like my father.'

'Is that an accusation?'

'No. It's just – it feels as though you're humouring me. Cheering me on to better things. Well done, Dougie, good boy. Pat-pat. Now try harder.'

'That's not fair.' The surly reaction wasn't like him.

'Maybe not fair, but true.' He stood looking at me with his head lowered. 'You've been so successful. My two minor promotions feel like baby steps by comparison. I'd hoped to be much more established by now.'

The sudden accusation was a shock. He had always been so encouraging.

'But it hasn't just happened,' I protested. 'You know how hard I've worked.'

'So have I, for much less,' he said.

I hadn't thought of his job that way. Men with Oxford MAs were supposed to rise to the top like cream in their chosen professions or careers, just as mothers were supposed to spend their lives tending to families.

For the second time in a week, my illusions had been jarred by a reality I had been too self-involved to perceive. Mum and Doug had been marking time while I soared, revelling in all the acclaim. I was guilty of being insensitive to the concerns of the man I loved and the mother who had done so much for me.

Lally had recognised a kindred ego instantly.

# 8

Doug enjoyed his new position with increased responsibility and said he was forging ahead at work. We saved up and bought a hi-fi, an electric mixer and a dishwasher. Life was groovy.

During our working weeks, that is. At weekends when Yselle went to English lessons or to see friends, we had the daunting task of being full-time parents to a lively, inquisitive six-year-old and the twins whose terrible twos had lasted into their third year. The continual squalling had given way to temper tantrums which they'd learnt not to inflict on Yselle but saved up for us.

I'm not saying they weren't lovable – especially when they were drifting off to sleep with their thumbs finally in their mouths – but they weren't easy either.

Both had my colouring: hazel eyes and straight brown hair, coupled with a fiery resolve to be as different from each other as possible. Tasha insisted on having her long hair tied back in a ponytail and refused to wear socks and shoes unless frostbite was imminent. Chloe viewed the world through a fringe like an Old English sheepdog and would only wear gumboots. Tasha danced, Chloe stomped. Tasha climbed table legs and trees, and was happiest teetering along high walls as she bellowed at everyone to look at her. Chloe hated heights and was happiest hiding in cupboards with all their stuffed toys, which made Tasha furious because half of them were hers.

What the twins had in common was Doug's determination without his anxiety. This meant an adamant refusal to listen to reason or consider anyone's needs but their own. If you tried to help or made a suggestion, they'd shout in unison, 'No! Me do it!'

Neither would be dictated to about clothes. Favourite garments were worn to rags; the matching white broderie anglaise frocks threaded with pale blue ribbons that Mum sent for their second birthday hung in the wardrobe unused. The twins favoured bright blue and red – Noddy colours, they called them – but if one wore red, the other wore blue. Pants were in, skirts were out. When cat-suits were all the rage, they wore theirs day and night until I had to buy two more so we could launder them.

These shenanigans coupled with Robin's continual questions and demands for games wore Doug and me down to the bone by Sunday evenings.

'You're always bloody busy and I'm on the far edge of sanity. We have to get full-time help,' he groaned after one fraught weekend, sinking into the sofa.

'Agreed.' I'd begun to wonder why we'd even considered having kids in the first place, a bad sign.

'Ask Yselle to find someone.'

Too late. When I spoke to her the next day, she broke down in tears. 'So sorry, Madame Anne, I cannot remain wiz you any longer.'

'Why now? *Please* stay. We really need you,' I begged.

'Because my mountain home is calling,' was all she'd say, weeping.

The predicament escalated to crisis point when Ivy announced that she was also leaving, to marry her new boyfriend and live in Manchester. I'd never been without help, much preferring writing to household chores and coping with anarchic children. It made me chillingly aware how dependent I was on the labour and goodwill of other women.

I phoned the au pair agency in a panic, dreading that they'd sniff, 'Our girls aren't prepared to do housework as well as look after children. You need a cleaning woman before we'll even consider your application.'

But the gods were smiling: the agency had branched out into the field of general employment, and on their books was an angel from Ghana. She arrived the day after Yselle left with tears pouring down her face, sobbing, 'I never forget zis family. Never!'

From the heart I said, 'It is we who won't forget. You've been a lifesaver. How can we thank you?'

Doug added, 'You're a beautiful person, Yselle.'

'You too. All beautiful! No need to sank!' She hugged me, then him, then Robin and the twins before rushing to the taxi we had ordered, crying all the way.

'I'm surprised at the waterworks,' I said as we herded the kids inside. 'She didn't strike me as sentimental.'

'You never know how people will react,' was his only comment.

Euphemia Ofay was large in every respect: big-boned, big-voiced, big-hearted. It was like going home the day she walked in and took over the house. She wore dazzling kente cloth robes with matching headscarves and armfuls of bracelets that clunked as she worked: silver, brass, ivory, bead, elephant hair. She boomed rather than talked and sang in a quivering contralto as she worked in the mornings. Afternoons were for the twins and Robin when he came home from school. For double her hourly pay she'd take them on at weekends too, a bonus that made all the difference.

'I need the money, see?' she told us. 'Husband gone, three sons at home with my sister, and I want a good life for them. Better than mine, anyway.' Her hoot of laughter rang down the street. 'Doctors or lawyers, I tell them. Businessmen, maybe. Not slaves. Uh-uh.'

'Surely you don't see yourself as a slave?'

'Never.' The headscarf twirled about her head like a psychedelic meringue gave an emphatic sideways shimmy. 'No ways. Uh-uh. It's my choice to work and you pay proper wages, unlike the last one. She wanted too much for too little. I walk out one morning, just like that! And I laugh all the way home. No more cleaning her stinky toilets. Nothing doing!' Bracelets clashed as she shook her fist.

'I hope you won't walk out on us,' I whimpered.

'Annie, no! Uh-uh. I like too much these kids. They make me think of my own boys, so far away. Too far.' She lowered her arm to knuckle away the tears coursing down her cheeks. 'If I stay here four-five years, work hard, save everything, I can go home with enough to give them the good life. You see?'

She was magic. We took advantage of our new weekend freedom as often as we could. I don't think the kids even noticed when we slipped away the first Saturday afternoon to spend a blissful night alone at a small hotel. Euphemia had promised to take them to the swings in the park, cook as many fish fingers as they could eat for supper, and tell them stories about her home village until they fell asleep. She knew how to keep them busy and happy, and they adored her. She was a much better mother than I was.

Though you wouldn't have thought so from my answers to the letters that poured in to my new column: *Annie Butterfield Advises.*

After I'd foolishly raved about Euphemia and my new-found freedom to Lally, she had said, 'Since my readers think the sun shines out of your arse, how about taking on another column? *Modern Lifestyle* needs an agony aunt.'

'Oh, no. The cooking's enough.' I was adamant to begin with. 'I've got other work and we talked about a book, remember? You can't ask me to do this.'

'I can, and am.'

'You can't! I won't.'

'Consider, Annie. Readers feel that they know you, so they'll trust your advice. And I'll pay well.'

'No, Lally. No.'

I went on babbling denials but she had become the most powerful editor in Britain and was an expert at putting on the screws. She offered a handsome contract on top of the *Fabulous Fast Food* one, for a combined sum that would allow us to buy the bigger house we needed. Euphemia deserved a decent-sized bedsitter and Robin was desperate for his own space that the twins couldn't invade.

Doug and I spent a week agonising over our options.

He'd say, 'My salary isn't high enough yet to qualify for interest payments on a decent-sized mortgage. Can we trust Lally to keep both contracts going for at least a few more years?'

And I'd say, 'I haven't accepted her offer yet.'

And he'd say, 'I don't think you should take on another column. Cooking and personal advice are completely different.'

And I'd say, being contrary, 'Not if you have an ounce of common sense. Agony aunting should be a breeze. Specially if we found a house with a separate workplace for me and a playroom for the kids on rainy days.'

And he'd say, 'I'm worried about over-committing ourselves.'

And I'd say, 'But we need a bigger house.'

And he'd say, 'Only top managers can afford bigger houses.'

And I'd say, 'Aren't you expecting to be promoted soon?'

And he'd say, 'You can never count on a promotion. And my salary isn't high enough yet ...'

Round and round in circles until we decided on a compromise. I would tell Lally that I'd try writing a few advice columns without a contract to see how the readers responded. In the meantime, he'd ask the London & Home Counties division of his firm to keep an eye out for a house that would suit us. When I suggested that he also sound out the personnel department about his future prospects, he refused point-blank. 'It isn't done.'

'I don't see why not. Surely young executives need some idea of what's being planned for them?'

His answer was a curt, 'You don't ask. You just work your fingers to the bone and hope someone will notice.'

There was an edge to his voice that I put down to his reluctance to question the bigwigs who ruled his life. There was no doubt in my mind that my personable, conscientious, well-qualified husband would continue to ascend his chosen ladder. Getting past the first rungs was just taking a little longer than expected.

My resolution to be more perceptive and understanding hadn't lasted past the next rung on my own ladder.

Instead, hoping to divert him from his worries over the prospect of a mortgage, I planned a fireside supper with our closest friends for my next column, serving his favourite comfort food: oxtail soup with garlic bread; toad-in-the-hole with baked tomatoes and stuffed onions; and chocolate éclairs.

The published cost of this meal, with beers to lubricate the toad-in-the-hole, was four pounds ten shillings. It went down a treat with readers' husbands and boyfriends, who begged for more. Lally said, 'Spot on, Annie. We've been wondering how to increase our male readership.'

I'd cheated over the cost which didn't include the bottle of Châteauneuf-du-Pape contributed by Susie and Xavier, or the box of Turkish delight from Ginger and Zeke. Or the Drambuie that Cuckoo had brought in lieu of her boyfriend, drawling, 'I've chucked the unreliable bastard.'

Euphemia joined us for the last course when Robin and the twins had been fed, bathed and put to bed, regaling us with stories about her Ghanaian family, followed by Zeke's memories of his Hungarian grandmother.

It was a wonderful evening. I hadn't seen Doug so relaxed for months, and decided that I must arrange more happy times like this when he forgot about job pressures. We were both so involved with our work and the kids that we'd neglected our friends. You get locked into the physical demands of a busy life and forget that you should be making time for fun too. And love.

Maybe a new home would give us more freedom?

# 9

Reading over what I've written, I sound like a tough nut: an uncaring mother with her face stuck in a typewriter, more concerned with her career than her kids, whom she has abandoned to the care of other women, or with pleasing her man. It was very important to please your man when I was a teenager in the fifties. As the twentieth century progressed and women began to cast off their chains, it became more important to please yourself.

But I'm not a tough nut. I love my family. Work came second when they needed me. And Doug was always number one. Making love was a vital part of our lives, frequent and passionate until the exhaustion of dealing with small and then growing children ate into our time alone together. Even when the years began to take their inevitable toll, our bodies were in tune, responding with the same delight. I adored his smell of apples and fresh bread, and the feel of his damp shower-warm skin in the morning. I loved the way his black hair curled into his neck, showing threads of silver as he neared his forties.

He said he loved my womanly body, which is full-bosomed and small-waisted above broader hips, and my energy. In the early days he liked me to wear my hair long so that it fell around us when we made love. And he told me I was beautiful.

Which I'm not. Neither am I the glamorous country housewife implied by my retouched magazine photos. Sweaters and jeans were my working uniform. And even Lally wouldn't cross me when I was in forceful mother mode, such as when Robin broke his arm taking a dive off a jungle gym and had to be rushed into hospital for x-rays, a plaster cast and cosseting. My debut column as an agony aunt was days late and for once she didn't make a fuss.

'Get my eyes clawed out,' she commented drily when I asked her why she wasn't ranting.

'As if.' If I had claws, she was a fire-spitting dragon with steel talons.

'I have a mother too,' she said. Adding, 'So now you've had time off, I want two more columns by next week.'

'You haven't read this one yet.'

'I don't have to. You're good, Annie. The readers trust you. It'll be a breeze.'

Agony aunting *was* a breeze. I introduced myself as follows in the first column and used some of it again years later to begin the last of the many handbooks I would write, *True Blue Superglue.* Reading it over now, I'm mortified by the patronising tone and repetitive anodyne phrases, though Lally said my advice was right on the button.

'Readers want guidance and reassurance with a minimum

of moralising. They need to be told they're normal and not alone, and to unload on you the feelings and worries they can't talk about with anyone else. You're it, darling: their free counsellor in *Modern Lifestyle*, the magazine that has it ALL.'

'My suggestions sound so corny.'

'Corny is what they want: great advice wrapped up in the comforting idea that they can control their lives if they really try. It's crap, of course. Life's a lottery and we both know it.'

'I don't see it that way.'

'Not yet. That's why you're so good at this stuff, Annie: all gung-ho optimism while you overlook bald facts you don't want to acknowledge.'

'Is that a character assassination or a compliment?'

Her brittle laugh crackled in my ear. 'You decide. And remember to keep using the word "partner" as discussed. Okay?'

The stuffy words 'husband' and 'boyfriend' and 'wife' and 'girlfriend' were passé, she'd said. 'Date' was the word for someone you were going out with, and 'partner' the preferred feminist term for committed couples, as it covered everyone.

Lally was well ahead of her time. She and her partner Una, a barrister, had been together for twelve years.

'Okay,' I said as her receiver crashed down.

***Annie Butterfield Advises***

*Annie calling! In this new column, I'm wearing my wise aunt's face instead of my cook's apron to give advice on your personal problems. I'm here to offer guidance and answer your most intimate queries. So lean on me, dear readers. If you have a dilemma or are in a predicament you can't discuss with anyone else, write to me and I'll do my best to come up with a solution.*

*Each column will begin by tackling an aspect of our modern lives. This month it's about choosing a compatible partner.*

***Annie advises:*** *Keep your head if you feel you're losing your heart. Take time to evaluate the new love in your life. Does he show affection without crowding you sexually? Is he kind? Honest? Does he listen to you? First and foremost, a partner should be your trusted friend.*

*Don't think you can change a seriously flawed person or a bully. You can't. Basic natures persist. More self-destructive mistakes have been made in the name of love than all the valentines ever printed.*

However old-fashioned she sounds today, Annie Butterfield had her virtues. The readers loved her. Letters came pouring in, detailing a range of problems that would have daunted a counsellor with years of expertise. Me, they almost overwhelmed.

*Dear Annie*
*I dont know what to do please help. My boyfrend goes inside of me hard for a long time until it hurts and when I say please stop he says if I dont let him he can easaly find somebody else who will. I love him what can I do?*
*Loreen*

*Dear Loreen*
*You are not alone in feeling uncomfortable with your relationship. Many loving couples struggle to balance their physical needs.*

*My advice to you is this: no lover has the right to hurt you or force you to do anything. Think carefully about whether he is the right man for you.*
*Annie*

A surprising number of women had discovered they were involved with cross-dressers. There was a major who went shopping in his wife's skirts and make-up, wearing high-heel shoes bought in an outsize shop. There was a surgeon who would only wear silk French-leg panties. A railway porter was turned on by his dead mother's petticoats. Their partners epitomised the quiet bravery of puzzled but loyal women.

*Dear Annie*
*My hubby is different. He likes to go out wearing my suspenders and stockings under his trousers, also a bra and panties. Now he wants me to buy him a dress and a wig so we can go out two girls together. I don't know what to do. He seems so normal otherwise, doesn't go for blokes and says he loves me even more now that he knows what makes me tick. Our sex life is fine excepting for his lipstick everywhere.*
*Starr*

*Dear Starr*
*If dressing up like a woman gives your husband a kick and is not affecting your relationship, there's no reason to be alarmed. Just aim for discretion when you're out together. Too many people still live in the partnership Dark Ages.*
*Annie*

Some personal dilemmas were far worse. There were men who demanded to be thrashed with whips until they bled, avaricious relatives, girls who slashed themselves, teenagers out of horror comics, nightmare children – and incest. I learnt that it happened regularly in suburban homes where brutalised mothers kept cowering-quiet for fear of losing everything.

*Dear Annie*
*I found out why my little girl age nine is always crying when I caught my husband coming out of her bedroom pulling up his trouser zip. He said if I tell anyone he'll kill her then me, and I'm scared he means it. What can I do?*
*Susan*

This one had an address. Within five minutes of my receiving it, Lally had notified the police who staked out the house and arrested the man when he returned home from work. He got ten years for child abuse. Their daughter was taken into child care and Susan disappeared. I agonised about her for months.

Some men were beating their helpless wives and children with a scientific precision that left no visible bruises.

*Dear Annie*
*I'm black and blue all over hurt like hell can't see out my eyes can't go in the street he's much stronger than me locks me up when he goes to work please please please how can I make him stop? He calls me Missy Mouse.*
PS *Got no family nor friends neither.*

*Dear Missy*

*You must have been able to get away from him to post your letter. Next time you have a chance, walk out the door and run to the nearest police station for help. There is no reason to go on suffering. I wish I could put my arms around you right now to give you the strength to make this difficult first move away from your pain and suffering.*

*Annie*

The avalanche of pleading letters had me screaming at Lally after the first month, 'I resign from writing this column! How can I possibly advise on horrors I know nothing about? I won't do it.'

'Calm down. I expected drama,' she said in her blandest voice.

'Thanks for bloody telling me.' I was furious.

'If you feel you need help from professional counsellors, Annie, I'll pay for their advice. Just write the stuff from your heart. As I've said before, you're good. The readers trust you.'

'You could have warned me this would happen.'

'If I had, you wouldn't have agreed to do it. And the magazine needs you.'

God help me, I was flattered. My head swelled along with my postbag.

# 10

Pat Quincey came into my life as the chief counsellor on *Annie Butterfield Advises* and became a friend whom I could phone (and still do) at any time of the day or night for advice. She was a clinical psychologist attached to a general hospital who helped traumatised patients to work through their ordeals. Now in her eighties, crippled with arthritis and in constant pain, Quince remains the kindest, most sympathetic and concerned person I know.

Then, she was a small, feisty, freckled person who would charge into a crowded waiting room chirping through buck teeth, 'Sorry I'm late!' then introduce herself all round, using the opportunity to sum up new patients.

One piercing look from those sharp eyes under a turbulence of foxy curls, followed by a few questions, and Quince would have a good idea of your problems.

She spurned classifications for gut-feel, which she defined as experience multiplied by empathy. She could soothe victims of violence with an arm around shaking shoulders and murmured words of support in their ears. She reassured me by saying I was a natural communicator between experts and needy readers.

'I can advise you what to suggest, but you're the one who turns it into the right language,' she'd say. 'I'm a clot at writing stuff.'

'Don't you believe it,' Lally said at our first meeting in her office. 'Quince has a brain like a razor, just can't be bothered with putting pen to paper. You're an ideal team.'

I think we were. The column ran for nearly fifteen years and Quince said more than once, 'The human heart holds more secrets than doctors and psychologists can ever hope to plumb, but we'll die trying, eh?'

'Amen,' said Lally, the fervent agnostic with her eye on the bottom line. 'Annie Butterfield' was reeling in readers by the thousands and paying both of us well. Doug and I were able to buy a new Vauxhall sedan. Luxury.

After the tribulations of Vietnam and Watergate, the world around us seemed to calm down and become more hopeful. The Suez Canal re-opened, North Sea oil began flowing and Mum reported from home that at last they were getting TV, 'For what it's worth. I don't have time to watch, but Dad likes to go to sleep in front of it.'

Wishing she lived closer for granny duties, I made time to sit at the TV watching Princess Anne marry Mark Phillips with the twins commenting on every royal detail, entranced by the pageantry and the uniforms. But it was hard persuading them afterwards that wedding dresses and veils were for big girls.

'You don't like dresses,' I pointed out, 'and veils would cramp your style.'

'What's that?' Tasha said.

'It's a thing you have to climb over, silly.' Chloe rolled her eyes.

'I don't mean that kind of stile. It's a particular way of doing things. It's—'

'But I want to get married and go in a glass coach with horses and lots of people waving flags,' Tasha insisted.

'Me too,' echoed Chloe. '*And* soldiers with swords.'

'Who will you marry?' I asked.

'Dad, of course,' said Tasha.

'I'll have Robin, then,' said Chloe. 'He can be quite nice sometimes.'

They rushed into the backyard to inform the potential bridegrooms, who were kicking a soccer ball around, and returned in a joint sulk when both declined the honour.

'Dad's just being horrible.'

'I'll marry a prince, then Robin will be sorry.'

'*I'll* marry a knight in shining armour. With a big white horse,' Tasha specified.

'Then I can have Prince Charming.'

'You can't. He isn't real.'

'He *is*.'

'Isn't.'

'IS!'

The discussion degenerated to a wrestling match on the floor which I tried to break up, saying, 'Stop this now, or I'll go back to work.'

Breaking off in a temporary truce, two small red faces glared up at me.

'You're *always* working,' Tasha accused.

'You're not a proper mummy,' Chloe said.

'What do you mean?' I whimpered.

'You don't make us cakes.'

'You don't take us to play group.'

'You're always *typing.*'

'You don't buy us ice creams.'

Wounded, I countered, 'But I bath you and read to you every night.'

'It's not enough,' Tasha scowled.

'We want you to be here *all the time,*' Chloe demanded.

'Like Euphemia,' Tasha said in a triumphant thrust, before they went back to wrestling.

I sat pondering my shortcomings until Euphemia bustled in and separated them, saying, 'Okay Annie, you can get back to your office now. I'll take these naughty princesses to the park.'

'Thanks. You're a star,' I said, with feeling.

'Maybe so,' she chuckled, 'but I love them, you know? Such women they'll be, like my Ghana sisters who never give up.'

'I feel as though I'm giving up when you bail me out like this.'

'You? Uh-uh.' It came with a loud hoot. 'Where you think they get it from, eh? You work hard, Annie. Doug also. This city life demands too much. You both need a break. Go away next weekend, make some love.'

She was right. Recently I'd been snappier than usual and he had been too tired to make love after coming home during the week to the evening demands of supper, chores, noisy kids, bath time and getting them to bed.

'You're always frazzled,' he'd accused the previous week.

'And you wonder why? Three kids are a lot of work on top of my other commitments.'

'But you've got Euphemia.' He said it as though I should thank my lucky stars.

'Of course she helps, of *course,* but everything's my responsibility,' I'd moaned. 'And I'm always interrupted when I try to work, while you just swan off to the office every morning.'

'I wish it were as easy as swanning,' he'd said, looking strained.

We needed to get away and grabbed the chance of two nights in a country inn, agreeing on the way there not to moil over our work and worries or even mention the kids. After a long rambling walk through autumn fields, Doug was his old self, relaxed and attentive over the candlelit dinner. We went to bed early both nights, eager to make up for lost time. How quickly love rejuvenates when you opt out of a busy life for a while to remember when it was uncomplicated and exuberant. He was ardent and tender, and our bodies sang together with long practice.

When we arrived back late on Sunday, Euphemia had bathed the kids, who were sitting in their pyjamas at supper looking like rosy cherubs. 'So,' she said, looking at our faces, 'Euphemia's remedy, she is working?'

'Oh yes. Thank you.' Doug hugged her, adding, 'You're a genius.'

'Agreed,' I murmured, watching his old smile curving up at both ends. The car radio had played 'Dream a Little Dream of Me' on the way home.

Though every year seemed more demanding than the last, all the omens were good.

Giving advice from the safety of a trusty typewriter was a piece of cake. I enjoyed it from the word go: deciding on a theme with the editorial team, answering readers' queries, soothing fears, making suggestions, consulting Pat Quincey or one of the other counsellors when I wasn't quite sure what to say. And trying not to chuckle over laboured handwriting that said things like:

*Dear Annie*
*My boyfriend wants he's cock rubbing all the time and it makes me come over all funny the way it gets big and hard and then leaks on my hand. Also I'm scared my dad will find out and call me a hore again.*
*Denise*

*Dear Denise*
*The men in your life don't seem to be at all sensitive to your feelings. Are you sure you need them?*
*Annie*

Lally didn't want to publish this answer, saying it was hardly helpful, as most girls were dependent on the men in their lives. I felt it was good advice and refused to change it. After a one-week standoff, she relented and it went into the next issue. Two readers wrote attacking my insensitivity, followed by thousands who wrote that my columns were the best part of the magazine.

'You were right,' she had to admit. Miracles do happen.

*Annie Butterfield Advises* took far less time than setting up the meals for the *Fabulous Fast Food* features. And its success went to my head. I began to think that life with Doug was perfect because we'd willed it. We'd been strivers, worked hard and been rewarded.

Three months after I'd signed my new contract with Lally, a colleague of Doug's in London property told us about a house in an insolvent estate that could go for a song at auction. It was on the Thames near Shepperton, a feasible hour to work by train and tube for Doug. We drove out the next weekend with the kids and Euphemia, followed by my parents who were on a visit to London, grumbling that they never saw their grandchildren.

The place was a dream: a south-facing Victorian double-storey on a freehold half-acre with a staff flat above a coach house, an orchard and a lawn sloping down to a jetty. Doug and I loved it on sight. Robin was in ecstasies over the coach house with its horse stalls, perfect for a fortress. Euphemia boomed delight at the prospect of her own flat, and asked if her boys could come over for a holiday in July. Dad said he'd heard that the fishing wasn't bad on this stretch.

Only Mum and the twins were negative. Mum said, 'Wouldn't you rather come home?' adding that riverside houses always had damp problems. The twins stood side by side with their fists on their hips, glaring down at the lawn.

'No park,' Tasha growled.

'No park *and* no swings,' Chloe echoed.

'But it's just like the park,' I tried to persuade them. 'Better than the park if we buy it, because it'll be all ours.'

'No swings *and* no roundabout,' Tasha insisted.

Doug squatted down between them. 'We could put in swings.'

'Want a roundabout!' they yelled in unison, then threw themselves down drumming their sandal heels.

'I'd have smacked your bottom for that, Anne,' Mum said.

I recited one of the mantras of modern parents. 'We don't believe in spanking. It causes behavioural problems later.'

'You're in for big trouble with those two, then.'

I snapped, 'Oh, rubbish. They're still little.'

'Little hellions, you mean.'

'They're just boisterous.'

'Spoilt, you mean. There's none so blind as a mother who can't admit her children's faults,' Mum said. 'They're exactly like you at that age.'

'I don't remember throwing tantrums.'

'Of course not. I've only begun to remember my childhood since I started painting. It's been a difficult process, sorting out the real me from the overlaid housewife and mother. I've realised how alike we are, you and me.'

She must have been dredging up the past in the fond belief that it would make her a better painter of naked men. I protested crossly, 'We're not alike! And the twins are just going through a stage.'

'A stage. The classic cop-out,' she said. 'Those two have nasty tempers, believe me. A spot of discipline wouldn't do any harm.'

Doug tried to bridge the troubled waters with his usual diplomacy. 'They're a handful now, but they'll grow out of it.'

'I wouldn't be too sure. They'll turn into problem teenagers if you don't keep them on a firm rein.' She directed an eloquent look at me.

'But I wasn't a problem teenager?' It came out as a question.

She laughed then. 'You had your moments. Champion sulker and a wicked door-slammer when you didn't get your way.' She planted her hands on her ample hips – my hips, damn it. 'Need I go on?'

'Well, well.' Doug was laughing too. The twins stopped drumming their heels and gazed up in amazement that their joint tantrum was having no effect.

'Mum!' What had got into her today? Wrapped up in her painting, she hadn't taken much interest in my children until now. Yet here she was criticising the twins and broadcasting my youthful failings with relish. I protested, 'I was okay most of the time, wasn't I?'

Her eyes – my eyes, damn it – shifted beyond me to Dad, who had gone down to the river bank with Robin. 'More or less.'

Betrayed and furious, I burst out, 'I wasn't a problem! I'm a success! I write two columns every month for *Modern Lifestyle*, which has half a million readers! And no, we don't want to come home. We're Londoners now, settled here. We just need a bigger house.'

The seething boast was a crucial turning point: I decided that we must have this house, whatever it costs, as evidence of my success. I often wonder if that temper-fuelled decision was the biggest mistake in my life, or one of the best things we ever did. How do you weigh a person's pride against years of happiness in a lovely home?

Mum said, 'Keep your hair on, Anne. Of *course* you're a success,' and went off to scrutinise the kitchen. Euphemia swooped down on the twins and bore them away, one under each massive arm, to climb the fruit trees in the orchard. Doug went off to talk to the building surveyor who had come to assess the structure and the cost of possible repairs if we decided to bid.

And I was left thinking, If I explode like that – okay, have a childish tantrum – when my mother gets on my nerves, how can I think of advising others about their problems?

## 11

Looking back, the first tipping point happened when we took on the hefty mortgage that made buying our lovely home possible.

I was the one who decided to bid up from our agreed limit at the auction. Doug wanted to stop, hissing, 'It's already too high, Annie.'

'No, it's not.' I raised my paddle again.

'We can't afford it. My salary won't carry more than—'

'Your salary and my earnings, remember?'

'Any more bids?'

The man three rows back who had been bidding neck-and-neck with me called out, 'Yes. Plus two-fifty.'

'The bid is against you, Madam.' The auctioneer was looking at me. I began to lift my arm.

'No!' Doug held it down. 'The payments will be too much.'

'Of course they won't.'

'They bloody will. I asked the head of personnel. He said the firm couldn't sanction a staff mortgage with payments higher than twenty-five per cent of my monthly salary after deductions.'

'What about my earnings?'

He looked sheepish. 'He said they can't be taken into account because you're a freelancer.'

The auctioneer repeated, 'The bid is against you, Madam.'

I hissed, 'But I've got contracts.'

'They make no difference. A wife's earnings don't count when it comes to a staff mortgage. We'd have to get one from a building society which charges higher rates.'

'Then that's what we'll do.' I raised my paddle. 'Plus another two-fifty.'

The bidding went up another thousand before I had secured our new home, with Doug muttering, 'This is crazy. We can't afford it.'

I didn't realise for years how the extra burden of debt would affect him.

Moving was a nightmare, even with Euphemia's help. The movers had provided plywood tea-boxes for packing the small stuff, but we ran out of newspaper for wrapping the china and glasses. Robin, trying to be useful, managed to pull a curtain rod down on his forehead and bled all over the white flokati rug until a plaster was found. The kettle got lost so we couldn't make tea.

The twins, almost four by then, tried to prevent the first pieces of furniture being carried out to the removal van by hanging on to the men's overall pockets yelling, 'No! You can't take it! That's our thing! Ours! Bring it back!'

Euphemia rose from her packing and swept them off saying, 'Uh-uh, my babies. Come, we'll find some ice creams at the shop.'

'Not babies!' Tasha bellowed.

'Big girls!' Chloe bawled.

'Okay, so we three big girls, eh?' she said, hustling them through the gate and along the littered pavement with a small hand clamped in each fist. 'I get two choc-ices, one vanilla. Me, I'm double extra chocolate already.' And her familiar hoot rang down the street.

I truly don't know what we would have done without Euphemia. When we reached the new house and the twins went hollering through the empty rooms, she said, 'Let them run. They need to feel the spirit of this place.' Fixing Doug and me with a glare, she added, 'You will make a nice home here, eh?'

'Of course we will.' I was brimming with confidence. 'It's going to be the best home ever.'

'I hope so,' Doug said. 'It's cost enough.' His determined frown was very much on my mind when I wrote about maturity in the next issue.

***Annie Butterfield Advises***

*The hardest parts of growing up and becoming a mature adult are deciding who you are and where you want to go, then taking responsibility for your actions. Some people seem to be born mature but most of us take years to grow up. Some never do. So how can you tell if you're mature, or getting there? Some of the signs are:*

- *You're reliable and stay calm in a crisis.*
- *You learn from experience.*
- *You take responsibility for your actions.*
- *You're prepared to admit when you're wrong.*

I ended the column with a nugget of the sock-it-to-'em advice that had become my trademark:

> ***Annie advises:*** *If you want to be a mature, well-rounded, dependable person who makes a great friend, lover and parent, grow up!*

Two letters epitomised the ensuing avalanche of fan mail.

> *Dear Annie*
> *You write about being a mature adult but I don't think they exist. Every single bloke I know would rather be in a fast convertible with his arm around a stupid blonde whose hoiked her skirt up to her fanny.*
> *Fed Up To The Teeth With Men*

> *Dear Fed Up*
> *Clearly you haven't met a real man yet. Keep searching. It's a rare breed, but they do exist.*
> *Annie*

The second was a variation on a familiar theme.

> *Dear Annie*
> *Here's my problem: three kids before I was 26, all out of the house now I'm 45, trained as a secretary though my shorthand's gone and my typing's rusty. I want to work and need the cash, but every time I apply for a job I get the brush-off, either because of my age (age??) or for lack of what they call 'recent experience'.*

*I've got plenty of life experience but nobody seems to want that kind.*
*Clever Clogs*

*Dear Clever Clogs*
*Use your nut, woman. Brush up on your skills with a refresher course, buy a smart suit and march into your next interview with a big smile and a diploma in your hand. Good bosses are suckers for hard workers with confidence and, yes, life experience – whatever their age.*
*Annie*

That reply resulted in months of controversy. Some readers wrote in saying, 'Go, girl!' but most wrote bitterly about being on the shelf and lonely, neglected by children or abandoned by husbands for younger women.

Lally was thrilled with the response and said, 'Contentious issues like that really boost our circulation. Keep stirring 'em up, Annie.'

I just wanted to weep over every tear-stained letter.

# 12

The student riots, hippies and music festivals of the late sixties and early seventies had been like movie scenery in our lives: fun to watch from a distance. We and our friends had growing families and more pressing issues to worry about, like school fees and mortgage payments. (Always excepting Cuckoo, who was now a specialist sister in charge of babies needing high care, and whose boyfriends never lasted beyond six months. 'Good men are hard to find,' she'd say, eyeing Doug.)

He turned thirty-five a few weeks before our tenth anniversary, towards the end of 1975. To celebrate both occasions, I planned a Saturday evening barbecue on the terrace of our new home for the next *Fabulous Fast Food* spread. He needed distraction because he had hit another stale patch at work: the manager he'd hoped to replace had decided to hang on for a few more years and Doug was talking of resigning.

Lally had given me a handsome allowance of twenty-five pounds and I invited various friends to a family feast. Besides contributing a West African sauce, Euphemia entertained the kids while we posed for Zeke's photographs. He started with a group shot of us standing round the barbecue grill in the twilight: the men in sports coats, grey flannels and ties, the women in variations of the trendy trouser suit – all with glasses of plonk in our hands, trying to look casually sophisticated. In the next shot, Doug presided over the sizzling meat wearing a chef's hat and a butcher's apron stencilled 'WORLD'S GREATEST COOK'.

When I look at the group photo today, I see that he is standing between Ginger and Veronica, Vron from school, who had turned up in London looking for work after a divorce. He has his left arm round her shoulders as he raises his glass to the camera, and you wouldn't believe from his broad smile that we'd been having a furious argument that morning about the barbecue, and what he called my 'outlandish bloody menu'. Which was: crisps with two dips (sour cream and guacamole); New Zealand lamb chops; pork spareribs (a new idea from America); chipolata sausages for the kids; Euphemia's hot chilli and okra sauce (too fiery for everyone but her); tomato and onion relish; cornbread; potato salad with chopped hard-boiled eggs; mixed green salad dressed with vinaigrette; toasted marshmallows; and sangria.

Inspired by Euphemia's exotic sauce, I'd consulted a range of cookbooks to make it an international feast.

Doug had come home late the night before and overslept. He came into the kitchen while I was whisking up the mayonnaise for the potato salad, grumbling, 'What's all this stuff for?'

'The barbecue tonight. Our friends are coming round with their kids to celebrate your birthday and our anniversary, remember?'

'Said I didn't want a birthday party.'

'When?'

'Last week.' He jerked open the fridge door to pour a glass of milk.

'I don't remember your saying that. Besides, it's not a party, just a fun barbecue. Lally's given us twenty-five quid this time.'

'Bugger Lally. I'm sick of being invaded by her stupid magazine. It's not fun. Can't you stop these food things, Annie?' He slurped down half the milk and stood glowering at me.

'But I thought you enjoyed them?' I was flabbergasted. Doug had always been so supportive.

'You're the one who enjoys doing this stuff. I put up with it.'

'Put up? You've been a great help all along.'

'I'm tired of being a help. Tired of these upheavals every month.' His face was pale and sweating, the frown lines deeply engraved between his eyebrows.

'Doug?' I went over to hug him. 'What's wrong? Did something happen at work yesterday?'

He pulled away, holding up his glass as though to protect it from me. 'Nothing happened. That's the problem. I'm stuck at my desk or in endless meetings while ambitious little shits like Baz Fuller get promoted over me. And when I get home hoping for peace and quiet at the weekend, everything's in an uproar over a barbecue for bloody Lally.'

'It's for you. I thought—'

'This house is supposed to be my refuge, but it's a stone around my neck. Don't you understand?' he shouted.

'Lally's columns help to pay for it,' I blundered.

'I don't *want* Lally's columns to pay for it! I want to support my family with a decent job.' He slammed the glass down on the table, milk exploding everywhere. 'This is too much. I'm going down to the river.'

He had taken up rowing again to keep fit, then found that going out on his own was a good way to banish work blues. 'It's like meditation,' he said once. 'Sliding between the sky and the trees reflected on the water. All you hear is ripples and the squeak of the oars and the thudding of your heart.'

I thought, Best place for him in this mood, and called after his retreating back, 'That's fine. Don't be late back.'

His response was an irritable grunt but I knew it wasn't in Doug's nature to let people down. As I went on whisking the mayonnaise and chopping onions and skinning tomatoes, I tried to understand what was making him so angry.

I tried, but didn't see. Not then.

After the main shots Zeke also took some of the kids toasting their marshmallows in the bonfire Euphemia had lit outside the coach house, and a brilliant sequence of her dancing round it in a gold-embroidered green and orange robe with firelight flashing off her bracelets. The export issues of that month's *Modern Lifestyle* sold out in Ghana, Nigeria, Kenya and South Africa, and created a demand for Euphemia's services as a 'fuller-figure' model for Zeke's stable of magazine photographers. All her earnings went into the savings account to give her boys the good life.

Her parallel career was still in the future that warm July evening. When Zeke finished the shoot, we shed our jackets and partied, fuelled by jugs of sangria – the innocuous-seeming drink with a kick like a mule. It must have been Euphemia who bedded us all down later on the living room carpet, bolstered by sofa cushions and our sleeping kids. It was certainly Euphemia who woke us in the morning with glasses of fresh orange juice and aspirins for our hangovers, and who fed the kids waffles with golden syrup and cream until our mortified visitors had recovered enough to drive themselves home. She was the genie of our household for five blissful years, a treasure beyond price.

Things Spanish had been in since the mid-sixties: ladder-backed chairs with woven rush seats, rugs with hot pink or turquoise flowers writhing on dark backgrounds, posters of bullfighters poised over swirling capes, gazpacho, aperitifs of fino sherry served in small-waisted glasses. Everyone had LPs of the 'Concierto de Aranjuez' and Fernando Sor guitar solos.

After years of mouli-ing, we also had blenders in our kitchens. Next summer I introduced cold soups to *Modern Lifestyle* readers in a special feature on garden luncheons. The variations were: vichyssoise *or* chilled cream of cucumber; rolled dover sole fillets with lemon sauce *or* galantine of chicken; Russian, Greek and beetroot salads; trifle *or* strawberry gâteau.

The summer luncheons and the autumn barbecues were so popular that Lally asked me to do regular seasonal features in an extra supplement. 'You seem to have a gift for divining what the readers need,' she said – a rare compliment. The most I usually got out of her was, 'Well done, you.'

'Both were a lot of work,' I hedged.

'I'll pay, of course.'

'How much?'

'One and a half times the usual?'

'Uh-uh.' Euphemia's emphatic negative was catching. 'Double.'

'Don't be ridiculous. That's extortion.'

I said, 'No, this is. If Doug resigns from his job, as he's threatening to, I'll also need more for *Annie Butterfield Advises.* You wouldn't want to lose your agony aunt, would you?'

'Extortion!' she shouted. 'Think you've got me over a barrel, bitch?'

'Right.'

There was a long silence, then she said in a voice that would have made gravel weep, 'Well, you have. I've made a mistake depending on you for my two most popular features.'

'I made them popular.'

'Under my direction.'

'But I've produced the goods.'

'At a price.'

'You said I was worth it. You said I pushed the circulation up. You said your readers think the sun shines out of my arse. And I've only ever missed two deadlines.' God, it was fun having her over a barrel.

Her answer hissed down the telephone line. 'Don't push me too far, Anne. You need me as much as I need you, but there's one big difference: I can find other people to do the work. A cordon bleu graduate for *Fabulous Fast Food.* A hot shot psychologist for the sob stuff.'

'Why don't you, then?' I knew she was bluffing.

'My readers wouldn't like it,' she conceded after a ten-second sulk. 'They're used to Annie Butterfield.'

'And I'm good. Admit it.'

'You're good. I'll pay what you ask,' the most powerful editor in the country said through clenched teeth. 'Just be aware of your limitations. You're a seat-of-your-pants cook who's been doing this for a long time, darling. Get stale, and you're out. However much the readers complain.'

Her icy 'darling' felt like a dollop of chilled soup running down my spine. I'd got carried away, baiting her. Living and working in that lovely house by the river with everything running so smoothly had made me reckless.

Now I thought, Anything can happen: Doug out of a job, the kids sick and needing care, Euphemia gone home to Ghana – and yes, I could get stale.

*Dear Annie*
*I'm the very experienced matron of an exclusive retirement home, and a lesbian. Most of my patients are elderly parents of wealthy people who hardly ever visit them. My lover and I live discreet lives in separate flats though we see each other at weekends. Last month we were observed holding hands by the son of one of our patients, who has threatened to have me fired for indecency by the Board of Governors of the home. What shall I do?*
*Benj*

*Dear Benj*
*Come clean in confidence to the Chairman of the Board. You'll be surprised how accommodating people can be when it comes to the kind souls who look after elderly parents so well that they don't need visiting.*
*Annie*

# 13

The altercation with Lally was a sharp reminder that I was as dependent on her as she was on me. If she dumped me and Doug resigned, we'd be in real trouble. He and I needed to have a serious talk about what might happen if we couldn't sustain our payments on the house. As usual in the early years of a mortgage, they had hardly made a dent in the sum we owed. And I was the one who'd insisted that we stretch ourselves beyond his limits to get what I wanted.

I tried to pin him down to a discussion the following weekend, but he refused to talk about anything but resigning.

'Surely you can't leave without another job to go to?'

'I bloody can. And will, if it goes on like this. We can always go home. There are plenty of good jobs there. I'd be in the pound seats.'

'But Doug—' The thought of leaving our comfy situation now to start again back in apartheid South Africa didn't bear thinking about. Schoolchildren had rioted in Soweto and violent police were shooting to kill. How could we move our English children to a country in growing turmoil, where Robin could one day be conscripted into the army?

'The firm is messing me around,' he growled. 'Ten years in the lower reaches of management, LSE courses, executive training – and for what? To get a pushy idiot from Australia promoted over me?'

I had met Baz Fuller at an office party. He was brash and full of himself, but no idiot. I thought, Maybe Doug is too much of a gentleman to do well in a large competitive firm where the Baz Fullers of this world fester? Being an Oxford and LSE man with a background in law and economics doesn't guarantee success in business, however bright, hardworking and personable you may be.

I'd learnt from my dealings with Lally that her company was ruthless when it came to profits. As long as my columns kept pumping up the circulation of *Modern Lifestyle*, I was untouchable. If reader interest dwindled, she'd dump me. Then we'd have to fall back on the freelance articles I was still writing for other publications – and they required far more research than the columns.

It was my fault that we had overextended ourselves. And I'd coasted along being so pleased with our lovely house that I'd lost sight of the fact that futures are chancy. Even promising careers like Doug's. At this critical point, he needed time to decide on what was best – and my full support for his decision.

I took his hand and said, 'Love, if you want to resign, we can keep going until you find another job.'

I'd handled our finances for years, when possible adding my freelance payments to a savings account. Doug had been happy to sign cheques and give donations to good causes, but in the grand way of busy executives had left the details to me. Which was why, I saw now, he was unsuited to the numbers games in the corporate world.

'You mean we can exist on savings if I chuck it in on Monday?' When I nodded, his face crumpled in relief and there were tears in his eyes as he gathered me into a tight hug.

The crisis blew over and Doug didn't resign, though he pored over employment columns and met friends in pubs to agonise about a career change. We talked and talked but he couldn't decide about anything, saying only, 'I've had my sights fixed on one goal for eleven years. Never considered moving to another company. Now it's too late.'

'What do you mean, too late? You're only thirty-six.'

He gave me a bleak look. 'That's late to start over again.'

'It wouldn't be starting over. You've got a good reputation in commercial property. That counts, surely?'

'Good isn't enough any more. Power-mongering little shits like Baz Fuller are the ones who make it.'

A few decades later we would be talking about our comfort zones, and job-hopping would be the norm rather than the exception. But things were different then for a man like Doug, born at the start of World War II to Depression parents. You were expected to work your way up a company, faithfully serving it in the expectation of being rewarded with a top job and later a good pension. He had articulated the philosophy at university: he was a striver. Not an entrepreneur, as today's generation is constantly urged to be.

He'd thought I was a striver too, but I wasn't. I was a lone ranger who could ride off in different directions, making my way at my own pace. I loved being free to choose my subjects and work at home. But the columns had made me much too reliant on Lally and her magazine. With Doug's career faltering, we needed an independent source of income to keep our home and the family going. When Euphemia left us to return to her boys, filling the crucial gap in our lives would be expensive.

She had become the pivot of the household. She bore the brunt of the twins, answered Robin's persistent questions, kept the house presentable, made the meals I didn't cook, bolstered Doug in his bad moments, supervised the garden and shooed away unwelcome visitors when I was working. She'd station herself on the front steps at the first sound of wheels crunching on the gravel, and if it was anyone other than a person in dire need, she'd wag her forefinger crying, 'Uh-uh! Go 'way! Annie, she's working.'

Brisk and adamant, she chased off charity collectors, girl guides selling fudge, Mormons, Jehovah's Witnesses, beggars and idle friends who wanted to pop in for coffee and a chat, for which I was profoundly grateful. I will always miss Euphemia's booming contralto and jovial hoots of laughter.

But we couldn't afford her if Doug walked out on his job, which seemed increasingly likely. He was harassed and grumpy when he came home in the evenings, often late, saying that he was putting in extra time to polish his marble. The children tiptoed round him at weekends and Robin spent more and more time fishing off the river jetty, encouraged by his grandfather who had spent most of his last visit down there, showing him how to set up tackle and bait hooks.

Robin was desperate for a collapsible glass-fibre fishing rod like his grandfather used, but Doug refused, muttering, 'We can't afford inessentials.'

I heard Robin ask, 'What's an inessential?'

'Something you don't need. Like this house.'

There was a long silence, then Robin said, 'But it's where we live. Why are you saying we can't afford it?'

'Because your mother wouldn't listen to reason when we bought it.'

'I don't understand.'

'Neither do I. She's a law unto herself. Likes wearing the pants.'

The way he said it followed by a mirthless laugh made me cringe, listening from the doorway. Was that how he really saw me, when I was trying so hard to be supportive and sympathetic? I didn't know what else to do but stand by him and hold the family fort as his expectations were gradually crushed.

Later Robin asked me, 'Why is he being so mean?'

'Just problems at work.' I reached towards his forehead to smooth the frown that was so like his father's. 'I'm sure they'll blow over.'

'I want my old Dad back,' he said.

*Dear Annie*

*It's this way with my Sammy: he's got to be top dog, no arguments. Even though I've got the steady job and he only does piece-work some days, other days he just sits at home watching the telly, he's the one who calls the shots. 'I'm the man of the house, so I make the big decisions,' he says. The thing is, I'm starting to*

*think why is it not me making the big decisions sometimes? I'm not stupid.*
*Geraldine*

*Dear Geraldine*
*Men have had it their own way for so long, it's hard for them to understand that women deserve equal rights. You could try chipping away at the rock-face by making occasional decisions yourself, or you could play it for laughs. Either way, don't expect miracles.*
*Annie*

# 14

We all wanted the old Doug back. His unhappiness coiled round our family rock like the roots of a strangler fig, squeezing us to cracking point. All through the sweltering summer holidays, I was ratty with the kids and over-solicitous with Doug, who reacted with growls that I was stifling him. Robin crashed round the garden and through the house in a gang of noisy friends with muddy feet, impervious to reason. The twins yelled their displeasure at everything. Euphemia took to singing martial hymns like 'Onward Christian Soldiers' and scouring any surface that showed a speck of dust, grumbling her disapproval.

'You people all too damn lucky, and you don't know it,' she accused me one day. 'Nobody's joyful any more. Uh-uh.'

Dismayed, I muttered feebly, 'It's just the summer. All this heat. We're going through a bad patch.'

Her swirling headscarf did an emphatic shimmy. 'Truly bad times you don't know, Annie. Is another thing. This house not an easy place any more.'

'What do you mean?'

'Maybe a bad spirit. Maybe too much argument. I don't know.'

I knew: Doug was stressed to breaking point by his job and money worries, and the kids were anxious. I pleaded, 'What can we do?'

'Not me. You fix,' she commanded. 'No more excuse, eh? Uh-uh.'

Life can turn on a single moment – a coincidence or casual happening that changes everything. There came a rainy weekday morning late in 1976 when I sat over marmalade toast and coffee in the quiet time after everyone but Euphemia had left the house, reading Doug's evening newspaper. A paragraph on the book review page mentioned a small Scottish firm headed by an entrepreneurial publisher who was looking for manuscripts 'of a popular motivational or self-improvement nature' and gave the address and telephone number.

It was a prescient move. The few motivational books until then had been earnest exhortations along the lines of Dale Carnegie's *How to Win Friends and Influence People*, the bible of salesmen and other strivers since the mid-thirties. In the post-war years when fifty pounds a month could keep a family in style, housewives were the norm and suburban bliss and Dr Spock reigned supreme. But everyone's lives began to change as more women went to work, costs rocketed and the financial industry girded its loins for the boom years of capitalism. Family groups splintered, grannies and stay-at-home mothers were old-fashioned, the existing pundits were out of date. People were going to need new sources of advice and inspiration.

I wrote to the publisher about my columns for *Modern Lifestyle*, suggesting that I could draw on my experience as a counsellor (it sounded better than 'agony aunt') to write similar books. I knew I had enough of a public following to impress them, though I'd have to use a nom-de-plume. It wasn't only because Lally would fire me for being disloyal. I also needed to be unidentifiable so my peers wouldn't know the depths to which I had sunk. The publisher answered by return of post asking for specific suggestions.

That's how it started. For years, egged on by the publisher, I cranked out a series of lucrative handbooks which were part of the groundswell begun by Shirley Conran with *Superwoman*. 'Life is too short to stuff a mushroom' became the mantra of my generation of women who scorned house-proud mothers. We were beginning to talk about careers and wanted information on correspondence and refresher courses, child psychology and changing relationships.

I wasn't in Conran's league and could never have managed her steamy romantic novels, but I wrote dozens of handbooks under the names 'Diane Usher', 'Helen Yardley' and 'Mary Goodman'. *Life Smarts, Divorced Kids, Bully-busting, Teen Dreams* and *Dealing With Anger* were all bestsellers. They gave us a crucial advantage: financial security that was not at the mercy of Lally's whims or Doug's bosses.

There were a number of bosses. He left the property firm after twelve years when he learnt that Baz Fuller had been promoted to director. Doug came home early that day, slamming into the house with a cardboard box of personal things from his desk.

'I'd never have a chance under that bugger,' he raged. With the alacrity of a successful rival, Baz Fuller had offered him a year's salary in lieu of notice.

I tried a soothing, 'Maybe it's for the best, love. You've been talking for years about chucking the job.'

His angry glare almost frizzled me. 'That was going to be *me* chucking *it*. This is *him* chucking *me*. He calls being dumped with full pension benefits a golden handshake!' It was a generous severance package for the time, but I held my tongue as he ranted on. 'He says that I'm too academic with no get up and go. After all those years of slave labour, this is my reward!'

'Maybe we should go home and start afresh,' I ventured. 'Mum says—'

'Not a bloody chance! That'd be admitting defeat. I've already registered with an executive employment agency. They say they can easily place someone with my qualifications and experience.'

But the property market was dicey that year. It took the agency three months to place him as general manager of the head office of a country-wide estate agency, with responsibility for commercial letting. 'It's a comedown,' he admitted, 'but they say that if I play my cards right, I should be prime candidate for the managing director's job when he retires in two years' time.'

Two years on, someone else got the managing director's job and Doug badgered the employment agency until they found him a new post: general manager of an air freight company in Hounslow where he seemed happy enough until it folded six months later. He came home in the middle of a Friday morning to yell as he flung open the front door, 'Guess what?

The company's been sequestrated and I'm unemployed again. Redundant! Superfluous! That makes thirteen years of hard graft down the drain.'

I shot out of the study as Euphemia came thundering down the stairs. Both of us must have looked appalled because he began to laugh and caper about, pulling mock faces and jibing, 'Never mind, ladies. You won't starve. Clever Annie will keep us in bread and butter.'

The laughter soon faded as he began the rounds once more.

'There must be plenty of available jobs,' I said over and over with my arms round him. 'You've just been unlucky. Find a better agency.'

All he'd say was, 'I'm not unlucky, I'm a complete fuck-up.'

Rowing saved him. He spent hours that month on the water, rain or shine, hauling on his oars. Though he wore a perpetual frown, the exercise did him good: he looked fitter than he had at university. I'm sure it was the aura of good health that landed him his next job as general manager of the UK branch of an American drug company in Slough, with an excellent salary and a company car.

'It's a good prospect, Annie. Stepping stone to the top job,' he said, with the relieved look of a man who was on his way again.

At last I could stop feeling guilty about the mortgage as we began to whittle it down. The kids could have extra lessons and nice clothes and bikes and canoes. Tensions eased. Doug enjoyed the new job, which he said was an interesting challenge, and came home at a reasonable time because the offices weren't across town. And we were able to pay Euphemia what she was really worth, including return air fares for her boys to spend two summer holidays with us.

Robin played cricket almost non-stop with the two oldest and Justus, the youngest, taught the twins to sculpt animals using the river clay at the bottom of the garden. The first summer they spent the entire two weeks creating a farmyard, drying each model in the sun to harden it before positioning it in a tableau on the paving stones next to the coach house, where the eave should protect them. Observing the tableau dissolve in the following winter's driving rain was a lesson in mortality that Euphemia couldn't resist pointing out.

'See, my babies, how all life returns to the earth in the end,' she announced after rounding all three of them up to slosh outside in macs and wellies. I watched from the kitchen door as she gesticulated under her giant umbrella.

'We're not babies!' both twins howled in unison.

'You don't mean *me,'* Robin said with as much scorn as he dared.

'Course not,' Euphemia lied. 'What I meant is, we all go back to Mama Earth sometime.'

'Can people melt?' Tasha gasped.

'No, silly,' Robin said. 'Euphemia means after we're dead. The worms eat our bodies and then the worms die. And they go back in the earth.'

'Then I'm not going to die.'

'Poor worms.' Chloe started crying.

I turned away and went back to my office chuckling. Euphemia would have to wangle her own way out of the existential hole she had dug.

The next time the boys came, Justus brought a safari reference book so they could create a savannah with African wildlife, from elephants down to dung beetles.

Chloe was best at modelling because she had a special relationship with animals and the patience to add the details in their pictures, scraping the clay with toothpicks to get their eyes and fur right, squeezing out ears and rolling tiny antennae with her fingers. Tasha liked making big animals – buffaloes with down-curving horns and elephants – roughing them out and moving on to the next without adding details, creating a whole herd while Chloe was still labouring over her first.

'Hurry up!' she'd mock. 'You're so slow. Isn't she, Justus?'

Ever diplomatic, he'd smile at them both and say, 'Maybe. But Chloe gets the little things right.'

'I get mine right too – look!'

'Yes, yes. Very good.' He'd blink at her from behind his serious round glasses, a mission-educated boy not used to challenging girls.

Euphemia watched over and fed them all, taking out relays of lemonade and biscuits, making hot dogs and aromatic meatballs for their picnics, and gathering them round her in the evenings to recount her grandmother's Anansi stories.

When I put the twins to bed later, they'd be babbling about pythons and leopards and wily spiders, and in awe of the sky god Nyame.

'He makes them all do what he says,' Chloe whispered.

'Like *you* when you're cross,' Tasha accused me.

'But you're not cross now, are you Mummy?' Chloe snuggled

closer. 'I like it when Justus and his brothers come. Nobody's cross.'

'Not even Daddy.'

'I wish the boys would stay for ever and ever,' Chloe said.

But of course they had to go home and the time came when Euphemia wanted to join them, saying that she'd saved more than enough for the good life and missed them too much. She left us in 1980 after five action-packed years during which Robin became an excellent batsman, thanks to regular cricket practice on the lawn sloping down to the river. Euphemia bowled tricky googlies and fast-paced deliveries to the middle stump while the twins fielded well enough to impress their dad, though they were hopeless throwers.

We all wept when Euphemia disappeared through the barrier at Heathrow in her brightest robe, waving a jangling arm and calling back, 'You people don't never forget your friend from Ghana, eh? Uh-uh!'

Finding a replacement took months. Robin and the twins were furious with her for abandoning them to the mercy of a preoccupied mother who was either hunched over her typewriter or chivvying them to help her with the household chores. Doug moaned that another light had gone out in his life, and he was damned if he was going to iron his shirts. So I did them, lambasting myself for being a fifties doormat.

Years later, I found that the twins had scribbled two words at the back of their built-in cupboard: 'NORTY! UFEEMYA!'

Sex problems are the staple fodder of agony aunts and I was no exception.

*Dear Annie*
*Your always writing about true love, but how do you know when its true? Guys say they want to hold your hand but they really mean your tits. They say can they hold you but they really mean get in your knickers. Im sick and tired of hoping for true love and Mr Right. Please tell me if they exist or am I wasting my time?*
*Wanda*

*Dear Wanda*
*The idea of a Mr Right for everyone is a lovely dream, and sadly there are plenty of Mr Wrongs. All I can say is, keep hoping and searching. Good men do exist, I assure you, though don't expect perfection.*
*Annie*

## 15

Budgie arrived in our chaotic post-Euphemia household with Zeke's connivance: he had photographed a disconsolate woman sitting on a bench at Paddington Station and taken pity on her.

One Monday morning he bustled her into the kitchen where I was preparing the dishes for that month's column saying, 'This is Wilma Budge. Her mother's died and she's alone in the world. She came to London to look for work.' Then he dumped his cameras on the window seat and gave me a hug followed by a disingenuous grin. 'I've said I'll employ her until she finds a job.'

Zeke was a collector of strays and lost causes. Ginger had broken up with him because she couldn't abide the lame ducks he sometimes brought home for a meal or a bed for the night. 'They either can't speak English or they *smell,*' she complained. 'I have to think of my position.'

'I'm too messy for her perfect flat,' was all Zeke would say.

Well aware that I was desperate for a housekeeper, he went on that day, 'I don't suppose you know anyone who needs a damn fine worker?'

I said quickly, 'Present company excepted?'

The grin shifted to devious. 'Of course.'

He was trying to foist his lame duck on me. 'Come in, Wilma,' I sighed.

She was matchstick thin under a drab sweater that hung over working jeans – the antithesis of Euphemia. Having put down a leather suitcase plastered with old travel stickers, she straightened up to face me. At least sixty I guessed, if not more, judging by the iron grey crop thatching the wrinkled desert-scape of her face. The jeans sagged over boots designed for route marches.

'Would you like a cup of tea?'

She nodded.

'You too, Zeke?'

'Sure, seeing as you're not ready for me to take the pics.'

'Sit down then, while I put the kettle on.'

I had turned away mentally cursing the interruption to my cooking schedule when the boots clomped up behind me. 'I'll do it.'

'You won't know where to find anything. Just sit down,' I snapped.

'No, you sit. I'll find out.' When I swung round, her khaki eyes were x-raying the kitchen as she ticked off, 'Tea. Kettle. Sugar. Cups. Milk in the fridge?'

'In the pantry.' I subsided into the chair next to Zeke, taken aback by her instant grasp of my kitchen layout. 'Teaspoons in that drawer.'

Zeke said in my ear, 'See? Two birds with one stone.'

'She's a sad old freak!' I hissed back.

'Wait. You haven't heard her story yet,' was all he'd say until the tea was made and poured and half-sipped, when he bent towards her. 'Okay now, dear. Tell Annie what you told me.'

Wilma Budge was sad but not as old as she looked, and no freak. She'd left school to join the WACs, driven ambulances in wartime France, progressed to a career as an operative in MI6, then retired early to work as a crane driver so she could live at home and care for her ailing parents. She ended the account with a gruff suggestion that she'd work free for a month's board and lodging to prove herself.

'I'm a bloody good cook,' she barked. 'Strong as a fucking ox. Work my arse off, given a chance. No frills, though. What you see is it. But I love kids. Always wanted one. Three would be a bonus.'

'Well,' I wavered. It was a powerful temptation. I'd never heard anyone call three kids a bonus. And having to keep the house even vaguely clean on top of my work was a daily agony compounded by our current diet of fish and chips and defrosted TV dinners.

'Just three problems,' she said, anxious that I should understand her limitations from the beginning. 'Prone to foul language. Won't get dressed up. Can't swim, so shit-scared of rivers.'

How could I resist her? Doug and the kids agreed within minutes of coming home to a batch of hot scones on the kitchen table, all the ironing done and me purring in my study.

Budgie – christened by Tasha – settled into Euphemia's flat and started whipping us all into line. She had formidable energy, scouring the house from top to bottom as washing snapped on the line, cooking two meals a day, baking up a storm and digging a new vegetable garden in her spare time. She read through a pile of books every week and never tired of telling Robin and the twins stories about the spies she'd known and the cranes she'd operated. She spurned aprons for men's overalls, but consented to abandon the boots in favour of trainers.

Budgie saved me from years of household drudgery, Doug from a resentful wife and the kids from an absent mother.

By the time the twins turned eleven, Chloe had become fascinated by small furry animals. We put up with serial colonies of piebald mice, then hamsters, before she graduated to guinea-pigs. When they reached double figures in their run behind the coach house, I tried putting my foot down, to no avail.

'I'm studying them, okay?' she said, and spent hours making notes about what they did and ate and how they mated and had babies.

Chloe knew all about reproduction and had communicated the graphic details to Tasha long before I broached the subject during a planned cosy chat.

'You know about your pets giving birth,' I began after some preliminary small talk, 'but do you know where babies come from?'

'Oh please.' Chloe radiated scorn. 'Daddy's got a penis, right? And he puts it in your fanny and squirts in some sperm to make a baby. Only there haven't been any more after us, so he hasn't since we were born,' she added, presenting irrefutable proof.

'Daddy's penis looks too small and wiggly to go in anywhere,' Tasha objected. We had never been prudish about our bodies in front of the children.

'He helped to make you two and Robin, didn't he?'

'Jesus had a virgin birth,' Chloe said.

'Who told you that?' We weren't churchgoers.

'Miss Jenks at school. She does regilious instruction and science.'

'That's an odd combination.'

'Not really, Mum. She says that God made every little particle of us and science is mainly particles, isn't it?' Chloe was squinting up at me, intent on getting at the exact truth.

'Particularly all the sperms and eggs.' Tasha jumped up and began to dance round the room chanting, 'Eggs and sperms, squirmy worms.'

Chloe jumped up to join her. 'Eggs and sperms, bilious germs.'

'Terrible terms!'

'Frumpy firms!'

They went off into gales of laughter and my chat was over before it had begun. I'd wanted to give them the spiel about daddies and mummies putting their arms around and loving each other like Doug and I did, but never got the chance. By the time they were fourteen, they knew far more about sex than we had collectively when we married. Doug and I had learnt the techniques of making love from each other. Over the years, as we became more attuned and took our time instead of rushing to a climax, our lovemaking became a mutual art form. Sure, we did it less often now but the longer intervals made the sex more exciting.

It was a long time before I considered writing a book on the subject, aware that my experience was limited to one lover. And I didn't tell Doug about *Making Love & Truly Great Sex* until it was published, because I thought he'd try to stop me writing about something so personal. But when I put the book in his hands and he'd read the title and glanced at the table of contents and dedication to 'DP – best friend and great lover', he surprised me with a proud grin.

'Is this what you really think? That I'm a great lover?'

'Of course. Though I can't make comparisons, since you're the only one.'

'Oh, Annie.' There were sudden tears in his eyes.

'Is that all you can say?' I was still smiling. 'How about "thanks" or "you flatter me"?'

'I don't deserve you,' he mumbled, turning away.

I grabbed his shoulders to turn him back. 'That's rubbish! You're a wonderful husband and father.'

'Bit of a rolling stone,' he muttered.

'General manager is a stepping stone to the top, you said?'

'It's what I was led to believe, strung along like a fool. Now I'm told that the big boss is always an American. Yours truly is out of the running.'

I put my arms round him. 'Not as a lover, darling.'

'That's a thought. I can always hire myself out to lonely rich women as a gigolo.' He shook my arms loose and headed for the door.

'Please come back.'

'Previous engagement, sorry.' He was gone.

Women weren't the only readers who needed advice from Annie Butterfield about their love lives.

*Dear Annie*
*What do women want, I ask you? I bring my popsy tulips, she says what, no roses? I buy her a box of chocolates, she says no thanks, they're fattening. I get her a diamond ring costing God knows how much, she says she doesn't fancy diamonds. Should I stop spoiling her, or what?*
*Esmond*

*Dear Esmond*
*Here's a radical idea: why don't you try asking your popsy what she'd like?*
*Annie*

*Dear Annie*
*Listen, us blokes have problems too. My wife bullies me for sex. Wants to go at it like rabbits. Says I'm lucky, other men pay for what I'm getting free. But I can't get it up to order, you know? Now she's giving 'that look' to my friends who come around. Is there something I can put in her tea to calm her down?*
*Sid*

I suspected that this letter was a put-up job – schoolboys having a lark? – and didn't answer it. Six months later I read a news item about a husband who killed his wife when he came home and found her in bed with one of his workmates. His name was Sidney Brown. I still wonder if he was the same Sid.

# 16

What is there to say about making love that hasn't been said before? Although I didn't quail from writing about something so central to our lives, it was a huge responsibility to give the right advice.

Quince agreed when I asked her for guidelines on sexual issues. 'You're treading on eggshells. People are so bombarded with conflicting information that they're not sure what to believe. Men and women aren't brought up to interact naturally with each other.'

'So what do I do?'

'Answer queries from your own experience.'

'It's so limited! There's only ever been Doug. We learnt together. It took time to get into sync.'

'That's the message you need to get over: learn from each other because making love is much more than having sex. Demands more and bestows more.'

'That sounds old-fashioned.'

'It's the truth. Always will be, whatever the current fashion in fornication.'

Dear Quince. I wonder what she'll say when I tell her about the headline I saw yesterday: 'ORGASM INDUSTRY CHEATS WOMEN'? The sub-heading was: 'Examining the myth of perfect sex.'

I never promised readers that sex could be perfect but I did say, again and again, that it could be damn good if you loved each other.

My handbook *Making Love & Truly Great Sex* grew out of a column I wrote in answer to readers' letters complaining that all the fun went out of lovemaking after marriage.

*Dear Annie*
*What can I do about my wife who says she just doesn't feel like it? I'm not a randy Andy always grabbing her. I bring flowers and ask her nicely but she's tired, got a headache, didn't sleep because of the baby, feeling low – nothing but excuses. It's doing my head in. I don't want anyone else. I love her.*
*Wayne*

*Dear Wayne*
*Those 'excuses' indicate real problems. Mothers of small babies can get very tired and low. I urge you to do three things: keep telling her you love her, keep bringing flowers, and look after the baby sometimes so she can get some sleep.*
*Annie*

***Annie Butterfield Advises***
*Achieving harmony with each other's desires takes time, but the reward can be truly great sex. Physical ease, generosity, tenderness and love are all components of a good partnership,*

*as are trust and loyalty – the superglue that binds couples and families.*

Superglue had recently appeared on the DIY market. The column went on:

***Annie advises:*** *Remember that sex means trusting your body to someone else. It's up to you to ensure that the trust won't be abused. I can't stress this enough: you alone are responsible for your body. Don't rush into sex. Wait until you're sure of your own feelings and your partner's trustworthiness before taking the plunge.*
MORE ABOUT TRULY GREAT SEX NEXT MONTH ...

Lally made extensive use of cliff-hangers to keep her readers panting for the next issue. When she read this first piece, she raised the print run and phoned to say I could skate closer to the edge of what was considered fit for a family magazine.

'Your follow-on column must be explicit,' she commanded. 'You've covered the lovey-dovey trust and harmony bit. Now I want the specifics: hows and whys and exactly what works.'

'No way.' I was emphatic. 'I'm not trained as a sex therapist and I'm not going to write porn.'

'Not even a purplish patch here and there?'

'No. Doug would be mortified. All our friends know I'm Annie Butterfield.'

'I wouldn't be mortified if Una wrote nice things like that about me. I'd be thrilled.' Her voice went all treacly – a weird phenomenon. You could crack Brazil nuts between Lally's usual snapped responses.

'Not if she did it in public.'

It was 1982, long before gay women in the professions dared to come out. As a barrister, Una had a lot to lose.

'Maybe not. But you could loosen the apron strings a bit more. Kick up your heels. Do a light fandango.'

'That's not me.'

Her renewed rat-a-tat laugh at the other end of the line could have been distant machine gun fire. 'You're more of a free spirit than you think, Annie.'

I said, 'You're wrong.' I'd met Doug when I was eighteen, and from then on, marriage and having a family had been my aims. Being able to work from home with increasing success had been an unexpected bonus.

'You forget you're talking to your boss. I'm like a customer, always right. And what I want is clinical information plus juicy details. Explicit down to the short and curlies, right?'

'I'll try. Promise.'

'You'd bloody better.'

She always reminded me of Mum and Dad's wartime song, 'Ac-Cent-Tchu-Ate the Positive'.

# 17

These were good years despite Doug's dashed hopes of becoming the big boss. As general manager, he'd had a lot to learn about the pharmaceutical business. He was sent on courses to familiarise him with product development and in his usual thorough way, studied long and hard. The job involved extensive travel in Europe and twice-yearly visits to the Chicago HQ, all of which he greatly enjoyed.

'New horizons,' he'd brag with a blithe wave as he left for Heathrow in the upgraded company car that went with a more important job, a mock-wood-panelled Ford station wagon.

'All very well for you, flitting about the world,' I'd grumble. But we both knew that I'd head straight for my typewriter, free to be Annie Butterfield, or get stuck into the current motivational book until he came home, when we'd make up for lost time in bed. It was romantic, having a refreshed and eager husband flying home from satisfying journeys and wooing me with exotic gifts. We both felt liberated: Doug into the heady world of executive importance, and I to write in the grateful knowledge that we were no longer in competition.

With Budgie running the household and the kids growing up, we were able to get away for occasional weekends in the country inn we'd found when Euphemia first shooed us out. It became a refuge where we could shrug off the years and go back to being just a couple in love, adventurous and playful, revelling in being able to afford a luxurious bedroom to romp in after an elegant dinner with French wine. Those weekends had a carry-over effect too. Everything ran more smoothly and the kids responded to our good humour and Doug's cheerful homecomings with high spirits.

The things I loved best about him were his determination, his up-curving smile and the feel of his body, whether vital with well-being or subdued when he was wrestling with his demons. I always thought he was the best thing that had ever happened to me, and seeing him as a father engaging with his children – interested in everything they did, encouraging them to venture further, aim higher, laugh louder – was fodder for the agony aunt who inhabited my professional curiosity, always on the lookout for wisdom to pass on.

These more harmonious times reinforced for me the doctrine that human beings function best when they have an environment and work they enjoy. Men especially seem to construct their sense of self around their jobs. If those are taken away, it's as though their foundations have crumbled or at least been severely shaken. I wonder now if the new generation of professional women will react in the same way, or if women's innate ability to network will carry them through loss of esteem or community standing? Euphemia, Budgie and Mum had such a strong sense of self, which I hope persists in my daughters – as I saw it growing even then in Robin.

He was in his early teens, a fitness fanatic who flourished at school, where he excelled on the sports field and managed to pass in the upper third of his class. He ate gigantic meals and burnt enough energy to fuel a dozen generators. His room had a punchbag and dumbbells and posters of his action heroes – astronauts, racing drivers, soccer stars and boxers. No girls so far, but he spent time at the bathroom mirror checking his face for pimples.

When they turned twelve, the twins asked for riding lessons at nearby stables. Within months Tasha was soaring over jumps yelling, 'Look at me, Mum!' and Chloe was currying the horses and plaiting their manes in the afternoons. She'd volunteer to turn the handle that kept the farrier's portable furnace glowing as he trimmed hooves and picked up the red-hot horseshoes with tongs to sizzle into place before hammering in the square steel nails.

'It's bloody amazing, Mum,' she'd say when she came home all sweaty and smelling of horse and burnt hoof. 'They just stand there and let him pick up their feet and bang the hell out of them.'

Budgie's salty vocabulary was having its inevitable effect. Like most children they could speak 'proper' when they had to – at school and when their grandparents came on annual visits between Scottish trout waters for Dad and art galleries for Mum – but lapsed into peri-London vernacular otherwise. Orgies of grunts or shrieks or farting would set off my three into gales of laughter with Budgie joining in. She'd started calling them 'you sprogs', and they loved it.

And I'd sit in my study thinking, They sound so happy. We're all happy now that Doug has a decent job again. Long may it last.

*Dear Annie*
*What is happiness? I know this is a leading question but I've been arguing with my friends who all say something different. One says it's getting everything you want, and then some. One says it's being in love with the right guy. One says it's doing things for others less fortunate than yourself (she's a happy clapper). My mum says it's putting her feet up with a glass of wine. I think it's just knowing that life is great. But how can you really tell?*
*Irma*

*Dear Irma*
*You can't tell – you just feel. So I agree with you. Knowing that life is great is to be truly blessed.*
*Annie*

My next 'truly great sex' column was controversial: some readers objected to its frank counsel while others begged for more. Reading it over now, with explicit sex advice in magazines and porn freely available on TV, Annie Butterfield sounds like a well-meaning granny. But I really meant it when I wrote it.

How naïve I was, even at forty.

***Annie Butterfield Advises***

*To continue our discussion on truly great sex, here are some things you may never hear from anyone else – least of all your friends (often as uninformed as you are) and parents (understandably reticent about the details of their sexual relationship).*

***Watch your signals***

*Men – especially when young – are flooded with imperative hormones that demand release. Women are different.*

*A man's physical heritage primes him to make the approach. He's already fired up when he asks you out, so you can't blame him for trying – especially if your body language is signalling that you're attracted to him. How far he goes depends on you, the one with the cool head.*

*Mixed signals confuse him – for example, if you come on to him all evening, then say 'No' when things get serious.*

***Women take longer to get turned on***

*This is why making love is often disappointing at first for women. If a lover isn't aware of her different needs, they may never experience truly great sex.*

*Young men take their cues from movies, magazines and friends who boast about being fantastic lovers. Trouble is, he usually comes long before she does, which leaves her unsatisfied and him feeling inadequate. The old line, 'Wham! Bam! Thank you, ma'am!' says it all.*

*Women take time to reach a climax. We need to be wooed and made to feel special before we can become aroused, which is why relationships are so important to us.*

***What is great sex?***
*Experienced lovers know that great sex begins with sweet talk and plenty of kissing, caressing and fondling. They tell each other what they like and what makes them feel uncomfortable. They go slowly, enjoying the journey, trying out new things or doing it differently to enhance the pleasure. They use their fingers and tongues, exploring new sensations. They know each other's bodies and erogenous zones like familiar road maps and are not inhibited. This is why mutual trust is vital. Most important: good lovers don't blab.*

***Annie advises:*** *Practice makes perfect. Making love is an art that improves with practice. The more you practise, the more magnificent your result.*

Lally was pleased when the issue with this column sold out. 'You're doing okay, darling,' she conceded. 'Pump it up into a book, if I were you. Someone called Helen Yardley made a killing with *Life Smarts.*'

It was a big relief that she hadn't realised 'Helen Yardley' was me. I was always afraid she'd recognise my style.

I managed a feeble, 'Good idea,' and *Making Love & Truly Great Sex* came out the following year, authored by Annie Butterfield. *Modern Lifestyle* ran a special offer and thousands of readers snapped it up, making it one of the self-help bestsellers of the year. In a gesture that astounded everyone, she held a staff cocktail party in my honour in the office reception area and called me 'a media phenomenon' in her brief speech.

Looking back, it was the high point of my career and our prickly but always rewarding relationship.

# 18

Doug had six good years with the American drug company before it collapsed. 1986 was a disastrous year when their much-touted patent medicine for reducing stomach acid was withdrawn from the European market because of unexpected side effects. The UK branch closed down and Doug was retrenched, which precipitated a severe depression that lasted for months.

He changed to the point where we hardly recognised him, unshaven and unkempt in an old dressing gown, shuffling his slippers like an old man. He slept for hours, got up late in the morning, and sat dully mesmerised by TV while his rowing shell gathered dust in the barn. Budgie and the kids tiptoed round him. I wavered between trying to buck him up and locking myself away in my study, working in a froth of rage over the feeble way my talented, promising husband had given in to black despair. Someone had to stay strong for the family and he'd forced the role on me.

It was a year when the news from South Africa was getting even worse: news bulletins showed graphic horrors like necklacings with burning tyres and cops flailing into crowds of protesting people with sjamboks. Doug's father had died by then, and I paid for his mother to fly over and join us so she could spend time with him. He was so withdrawn that he hardly noticed she was there. After days of begging him to talk to her, she said sadly, 'He used to be such a lovely open boy, but I can't get through to him now.'

'He's had too many hard knocks. It's so unfair.'

She gave me a dark look. 'Life is unfair. His father never had the chances he had, Oxford and all. But those places gave him funny ideas. Maybe he's not cut out for business. We thought—'

When she hesitated I said, 'What, Ma?'

She was a small, neat woman with fingers so gnarled with arthritis that she could no longer use a sewing machine. Instead she tatted, and her regular birthday gifts of doilies piled up in our camphor chest. I'd taken some out to drape over occasional tables and sofa backs before she came, and would put them back into their fragrant tomb when she left.

'Pa and I thought he'd make such a lovely lawyer,' she said with a wistful smile. 'We've always been so proud of him.'

She and Budgie scurried round the kitchen making his favourite dishes and snacks to tempt him, with little success. He said what he ate tasted like sawdust. Soon she flew home again, looking older and sadder. Budgie said as we waved her off at the airport, 'She's like a sparrow with broken wings.'

My parents rallied round too. Dad had retired and they decided to spend the summer in England, renting a garden flat down the road. He volunteered to do the school runs. Mum helped me to get Doug admitted to the Maudsley Hospital in South London, which our GP recommended for its pioneering work in cognitive behavioural therapy coupled with medication.

'Treatment of depression is improving all the time,' he reassured us, adding, 'Believe me, this is usually a temporary condition.'

'Can we believe him?' I asked Mum after we'd left Doug trudging behind a nurse down a long corridor, his shoulders hunched in submission.

'You have no alternative,' she said. 'Buck up, darling. We'll stay on as long as you and the children need us. And there's always Budgie for moral support.'

She put on hold the painting classes she had signed up for at a community centre in Richmond to be a constant presence in the house, reassuring all of us that Doug's illness was temporary.

Tasha kept saying, 'He's not sick, he's loony, Gran.'

And Chloe echoed, 'Loony,' in a frightened whisper.

'Don't be silly. He's ill and needs proper treatment, that's all. His doctors say that he'll be fine in a couple of months when it starts to work.'

'Two months! Poor bugger,' Budgie muttered.

'And I expect you kids to support your mother and Budgie by being kind and helpful.' Mum fixed Robin with her over-the-specs glare I'd almost forgotten. 'You're the man of the house until your father returns. Act like one.'

'I'll try,' Robin said, and for a moment looked so like Doug when he was young and resolute that I had to turn away to hide my tears.

They tried hard. I'd never known them so thoughtful and tidy. The twins stayed away from the stables and did their homework without being told. Robin insisted on doing Doug's chores: putting out the rubbish bags on collection days, replacing light bulbs and locking up the house at night. Budgie held the fort on the domestic front while I struggled to turn out my cooking features and columns with a heart like a lead weight.

Doug turned his face to the wall when we went to visit him. His doctors said we were not to take it personally – rejection was a common symptom of clinical depression – but it was hard not to. He had become a stranger we couldn't touch without his shrinking away. Until those visits to the silent wards in the Maudsley, I'd never realised how many people succumbed to unbearable pressures in their daily lives.

*Dear Annie*
*My husband's gone, says he's never coming back, and the kids are driving me round the bend. They act like wild animals and don't listen to a word I say. Sometimes I want to throttle them. Other times I feel so low that I want to take a whole bottle of aspirins and never wake up. Please help. I'm so alone.*
*Desperate*

This letter came with an address which I phoned through to Quince, asking her to pass it on to Welfare for urgent attention. I was afraid that Desperate would be beyond help by the time *Modern Lifestyle* appeared two months later with my reply. Thank goodness they reached her in time.

I felt equally alone, even surrounded by the family. Doug had been beside me for nearly twenty years and now he was in a very dark place, leaving everything to me.

The agony columns began to cover an ever wider spectrum of problems as the eighties progressed. Besides the usual queries from teenagers begging for acne remedies, wives with embarrassing black eyes, impotent lovers, quailing sons of domineering fathers, and panicky girls who'd made one mistake and found themselves pregnant, Annie Butterfield had to answer people who wanted a sex change, boys who had been molested, men who feared coming out as gay. The dogged bravery of many lives was inspiring.

There had been a radical change in home entertaining too. Meals that ran along predictable grooves gave way to casual spreads and unusual recipes winkled out of ancient grandmothers and Moroccan camel herders. Elizabeth David's pioneering Mediterranean cookery and Len Deighton's ingenious comic strips were old hat in gourmet kitchens. Now the celebrities were sociable entrepreneurs like Robert Carrier – risen like an affable phoenix from classic French cuisine to popular TV – and Prue Leith, whose cookery courses were booked months in advance. Octopus and Hamlyn reigned supreme as publishers churned out cookbooks illustrated with luscious full-colour photographs.

My cookery columns were simply called *Fabulous Food* now; '*Fast*' had been dropped when 'fast foods' became the generic term for hot dogs, hamburgers and pizzas. Since the success of *Truly Great Sex*, Lally's annoyance with me had simmered down to the occasional irritable outburst like, 'Where's the copy for next week? You're late.'

'No, I'm not. You said I had five days' grace.'

'When?'

'When Zeke messed up his pics and I had to cook the whole meal again so he could re-shoot. Remember?'

There was a grudging, 'It's just that you're usually so prompt,' before her receiver crashed down.

I made damn sure my copy was prompt. The readers were still big Annie Butterfield fans, but that could change as quickly as a food fad.

'You should be covering a bigger range of food issues,' she snapped next time she called.

'What do you mean?'

'Go into the new delis and see what they're dishing up. I've seen cheeses multiplying like rabbits recently. Pastas in a dozen different shapes. Bottled salad dressings, for pete's sake.'

There weren't any delis near where we lived, but I made the trek into the West End and did a swing around the markets, a number of new delis in Soho, Fortnums and Harrods Food Hall. The patronising old butchers and fishmongers wearing jaunty hats were a dying breed. In their place were stylish young men and women in striped aprons discoursing about the particular mould in Gorgonzola and how to ripen imported Lebanese figs.

I needed to up my culinary game, or Lally would dismiss me as passé.

Under the *Fabulous Food* strap line, I did special features on olive oils (virgin, extra virgin and cold pressed were new terms then), varieties of lettuce, home-made mayonnaise, different kinds of rice, uncommon herbs (rocket, salad burnet, chervil) and exotic spices (cardamom, star anise, fenugreek). Budgie's vegetable garden starred in a four-page spread on vegetarian cooking in which I wrote about the glories of fresh baby vegetables, lightly cooked and served glossed with melted butter or yogurt and fresh herbs.

Just before Doug came home, I created a summer luncheon for Zeke, Lally and her partner Una, Xavier and Susie on the lawn down by the river. Vron and Cuckoo, both still in London, came too and we talked about organising a reunion of the Fearsome Foursome if we could lure Jude away from the remote mission clinic in the Congo where her order had sent her during an outbreak of cholera. After much laughter we tucked into: stuffed tomatoes with avocado fans; fish terrine with lemon thyme mayonnaise; cold fillet of beef with just-warm baby potatoes and a mustard dressing; mange-tout and artichoke salad; and passion fruit pavlova with whipped cream.

Budgie had become my invaluable helper in the kitchen and volunteered to serve the meal so I could relax and enjoy myself for a change. She caused a sensation by appearing with the first course in a blouse and skirt enveloped by a starched white pinny, set off with clumpy sandals.

'What's happened to the overalls?' I whispered as she bent over me with the plate of stuffed tomatoes.

'In the washing machine. Didn't want to let the side down,' she hissed.

'You look extremely elegant,' I teased.

'Fucking uncomfortable, though.' She chuckled and moved on.

It was a warm sunny weekday with hovering dragonflies and the children at school. Lally, looking like a flirty stick insect in gauzy drapes, took it on herself to style the dishes before Zeke took his pics. At the end of the meal she said, 'That was excellent, Annie. The readers will love the setting and the light food. Well done, you.'

'I'm flattered. Thanks.'

And I meant it. With Doug out of action for an unpredictable time and without a pension, my family's well-being was more dependent on her than ever. Some of my anxiety was reflected in Annie Butterfield's answers at that time.

*Dear Annie*
*You always so shure of evrything how can I be shure too? All I have is questins never ansers I just don't no if what I do is the rite thing or a big mistake.*
*Our Dawn*

*Dear Dawn*
*I am by no means always sure – or right. All I can say to you is, believe in yourself and trust your instincts to help you to do the right thing. Remember that nobody is perfect. All of us make mistakes. Often.*
*Annie*

# 19

Doug was in hospital for over two months under a regime of daily sessions with a psychotherapist and a powerful new antidepressant that knocked him out to the point where he could only mumble when I saw him. I didn't often take the children with me because they were so distressed by his dazed indifference.

'He's not *Dad* any more,' the twins would sob on the way home, while Robin clenched his jaw and looked out the window, suppressing his own tears.

'He'll come right, we promise,' Mum and I kept saying. 'It's a temporary chemical imbalance which the medication is correcting. His doctors are very pleased with his progress.'

It took longer than they'd hoped, but Doug did recover his spirits and came home with a tentative smile saying, 'Sorry about that. I just cracked up. Better now, though. Better and stronger. Need a bit of time to get back on my feet again.'

He was pale and quiet but refused to be treated like an invalid, working on his fitness by rowing every day, taking long walks and playing cricket with the kids on the lawn. Looking down at them one afternoon, I wondered how long the reprieve would last. I was frowning when I answered the telephone.

'That you, Annie?' It was Vron's voice, sounding strained. She was a thinner, more brittle Vron now, whose long brown hair had been replaced by a geometric crop dyed auburn. A brusque manner made it hard to recapture the easy friendship we'd had at school. Her divorce had been bitter and left unhealed scars.

I said, 'Yes, it's me. What's wrong?'

'There'll never be a Fearsome Foursome reunion.' Her voice quivered. 'Jude's been murdered.'

'Oh no.' I couldn't breathe.

'She stayed on alone to keep the clinic open in a village that was overrun by rebel soldiers. They –' Vron sobbed the last words '– gang-raped her before killing her with machetes.'

Jude, who was angry and swore like a trooper because she missed her parents and home in Uganda. Jude who'd said, 'I wouldn't let anyone put his tongue in my mouth. Other people's spit smells,' gang-raped by murderous thugs. Our friend had stayed at her dangerous post to look after sick people, while Doug and I were feeling sorry for ourselves in safe suburban England because he had lost his job. Life wasn't just unfair, it was a cosmic practical joke played on innocent victims.

That's what we told each other, Vron, Cuckoo and I, after the memorial service for Sister Judith, late of Uganda, at Westminster Cathedral. Her death was like a bell ringing, 'Be grateful for what you have!' We were a subdued threesome who sat having coffee before going home.

By the end of the summer Doug was fit and tanned again, looking forward to finding a job and getting back to work. He registered with a new executive placement organisation whose seriously suited consultants assured him that he'd walk into a top position, no problem, with his qualifications and experience. Mum and Dad flew home, no doubt feeling that they had done a good job supporting me.

But as the weeks dribbled into autumn and the interviews for jobs he considered good enough were followed by regretful letters, he began to slide back into despondency. Most of the interviewers told him that he was over-qualified. 'All those courses, you know,' one personnel officer had said, implying a desperation to acquire skills when in fact it was Doug's thoroughness that had made him eager to learn more. When his qualifications and experience seemed to be right for the job, his patchy track record told against him.

'They don't make allowances for adverse circumstances,' he seethed. 'I can't win. If I'm not over-qualified, I'm a questionable long-term prospect. But how can I be a long-term prospect if I keep getting retrenched? The corporate system fails people like me who get trapped in situations beyond our control.'

'It's iniquitous,' I said.

'Bugger that. It's a skewed verdict. I've worked damn hard.'

Haunted by Jude's unspeakable death, I was finding it difficult to keep up my quota of wifely sympathy. Doug was fit, strong and alive. He'd find a job. And I was weary of hearing how lucky I was to have a rewarding career that had fallen into my lap. I'd worked damn hard too.

*Dear Annie*
*Listen I know you supposed to stand by your man but my ones a stinker whose at everything in skirts never mind if they look like the backside of a bus, Iv'e had the bastard in chunks, wouldnt mind if he dropped dead in fact I'd be dancing on he's grave shouting hallylooya. So what do I do now???*
*Rita Hayworth*

*Dear Rita*
*Get advice from a good lawyer, darling. Legal Aid is the place to go.*
*Annie*

Robin's school held a fund-raising fête and Doug and I ran a Greek stall that the parents enjoyed, though the kids turned up their noses at the exotic food: pita bread; bowls of hummus, tahini, taramasalata and skordalia; lamb souvlakia; Greek salad; and baklava.

He was a great help chatting up thc mothers and at the barbecue where people grilled their lamb, but on the way home in the car afterwards he growled, 'Damn it, Annie. We make money hand over fist for the school and I can't do the same for us.'

I said (the usual stuck record), 'I'm sure there'll be something soon.'

'If a decent job ever does pitch up, it'll be too late. I'm forty-bloody-three. Over the hill. Verging on unemployable.'

'Unlucky, rather.'

He shot back, 'You're always saying that, as though it will

make me feel better. Well, it doesn't! I'm sick and fucking tired of being told I'm unlucky. I want to hit the jackpot like you did.'

As the accusation hung in the air, Robin said from the back seat, 'You don't let me use the f-word, Dad, even though Budgie's allowed.'

'You don't need to use it. I do.'

'Why?'

'Because it's how I feel. Because I'm fed up.'

'It's not my fault—' I stopped.

'That I'm a failure? Quite true. It's mine. The big deal with the Rhodes Scholarship and an Oxford MA who thought he was going to conquer the world, only to become a perpetual executive in waiting. Remember how I talked about being a striver? Well, I strove all right. Mightily. But never got there. The Baz Fullers shove me aside as they smarm their oily way to the top—'

I let him run on because he was unstoppable in that mood. My lovely Doug had turned into a sour, hostile has-been. Robin was silent in the back seat. When we got home, I heard him go upstairs and into the twins' bedroom and close the door.

They'd be worrying about their father's outburst, wondering if it was a sign of impending divorce. From my years of counselling teenagers as Annie Butterfield, I knew that divorce was a terrifying threat. How could I let them know it wasn't – would never be – an issue without demeaning Doug?

I couldn't say, 'Don't worry about Dad and me, he's just unhappy because he can't find the right job and feels like a failure. We love each other. I'll keep our home going until he finds his feet.'

His pride was taking a hammering. I couldn't bang in any more nails, even to set their minds at rest.

## 20

As the year dwindled into winter and 1987 crept in, Doug seemed to pull himself together. He consulted other employment advisers, went for interviews, rowed on the freezing river and spent time with the children or doing jobs round the house. Robin, who had blossomed into an all-round sportsman, was thrilled to have a dad who was available to drive his teams to school matches.

But Doug needed constant reassurance when the interviews didn't produce results. 'You're hogging all the glory,' he said to me more than once.

'Annie Butterfield' had become an icon as the *Fabulous Food* spreads evolved from advice on inexpensive socialising, to guidance on all aspects of entertaining, to a series on the celebrity cooks emerging from the anonymous steam of restaurant kitchens.

It was always a struggle to suppress the tears he loathed. I repeated the mantra, 'Please don't say that. We've always been a team. What happens outside our family isn't important.'

Words to staunch his haemorrhaging self-esteem. It had

begun to show now, in deeper frown lines and the glint of silver in his black hair. The up-curving smile had vanished. There was a bite of sarcasm in the things he said. His suits were no longer new and his shoes were scuffed. Doug wasn't striving any more, he was struggling.

My work for Lally and the motivational handbook publisher kept us afloat. Being an agony aunt had given me an invaluable resource to draw on for ideas: an archive of letters detailing people's problems. As well as Quince, I was able to call on a panel of professional advisers – psychologists, social workers, trained counsellors – for guidance on how best to answer them.

The issue of feminism was of growing concern to many parents, who wrote things like, 'I know boys and girls are supposed to be brought up equal nowadays, *but*—'

The litany was always the same. Boys and girls act differently. They want different things. Boys don't want to play with dolls and tea sets. Girls hate cap guns because they make too much noise. Boys couldn't care less what they wear (though this was changing, fast).

I thought it would be a good subject to tackle, and my next big seller after *Making Love & Truly Great Sex* was a handbook advising parents how to manage children's different needs.

From direct observation I can vouch that being able to throw a ball far and well is a male characteristic, as are large clumsy movements, an obsession with cars and speed, and – borne out by Doug and Robin – the inability to find things. They could look straight at a clean shirt or a cricket bat or a pair of socks and not see them. Engine parts ditto. Doug had bought a rusting old Austin 6 from a scrap dealer and parked it in one of the horse stalls in the coach house where he and Robin spent hours tinkering. Engine parts covered in black grease lay around on newspapers all over the house, but essential bits could never be found when they were needed.

Robin and his friends were also much more guarded than the twins – especially Tasha, who threw herself with gusto into everything she did. She loved climbing trees and galloping in a circle clutching the crossbar of the giant-stride Doug had hung in the willow tree near the jetty. The big thrill was the far quadrant of the circle where she could soar above the river yelling, 'I'm a jet plane!' If she wasn't up that tree with her nose in a book, she was sliding down the banisters or singing songs from *Cats* at the top of her voice.

Tomboys aside, my readers maintained that girls are more eloquent and communicative, good with finicky jobs and more sensitive to nuances than boys. At any rate, these were some of the examples given and I wove them into what I believe was a useful little book. Of course, it's been superseded by the avalanche of child-raising advice for young parents now.

My handbook guru believed that clever, catchy titles and jackets in primary colours were essential for potential bestsellers. I suggested *Adam & Eve & Pinch-Me* for this one, after the hoary old children's trick, and it sold in record numbers. Lally's book editor gave it a rave review in *Modern Lifestyle* and recommended it to me, saying, 'You've got to read this, Annie. Diane Usher's ideas are really helpful.' Lally herself suggested that I use it as a reference book for *Annie Butterfield Advises,* then in its twelfth year.

The compliments spurred me on to greater efforts. It was so easy. All I had to do was decide on a subject, articulate it in a punchy first chapter, then create a step-by-step programme to cope with the problems involved. Given a month's research, I could knock off a handbook in a few weeks. After *Adam & Eve & Pinch-Me,* I wrote *Faith & Faithfulness, Real Relationships* and *Family Matters – A Guide to Family Law.* I also did little single-theme cookbooks: *Brilliant Brunches, Spiffing Suppers, Divine Dinners, Stupendous Soups, Baking Bonanza,* etcetera.

At least a dozen books helped us through that hard year. They paid for the mortgage and all the extras: school fees, clothes, sports equipment, long-distance flights for the kids to visit their grandparents in South Africa (I was too busy and Doug refused to go), home office costs and Budgie, now indispensable. If Doug was out or moping and I was hunched over the typewriter, she expanded her activities to deal with school lifts, blocked drains and homework, with a particular focus on correct English.

'You sprogs must learn when to use a word for the optimum effect, and when to keep your effing trap shut,' I heard her telling them once. 'Good speakers and writers use language like a dagger: it must be sharp and to the point. No waffling. No bullshit. Bring me that essay, Robin. Show you what I mean.' Budgie's years of reading and writing the succinct reports required by MI6 made her the best English teacher they ever had.

She was my tower of strength and Doug's ally on the emotional trampoline we were all learning to navigate, always ready to jump onto a spot that would bounce him upwards.

Quirky little Budgie in her perpetual sweatshirts and work

pants or overalls, habitually earth-stained or covered in flour, got on well with Euphemia when she came to see us on a visit to England, arriving in a taxi with her three boys, now well-mannered young men in suits and bright ties.

'Look at my boys now,' she boomed. 'No doctors, uh-uh! No lawyers. But one in the bank, one in business and one in the university. Not bad, eh?'

They all beamed at us.

'Not bad at all.' Doug was always cheered by her ebullience.

'You people help me so much.'

I said, 'You're the one who did the helping. You worked hard to look after our family and give your boys the good life.'

The memorable swirling head-dress gave a vigorous nod. 'I work hard and you pay well. Also you treat me okay. Double okay. So, we bring our thanks.' She dumped the large plaited-palm basket she had been carrying and delved into it, pulling out a riot of fabric. 'Weavings from Ghana for each and every one.'

There were vivid cotton bedspreads for Robin and the twins and a double one in woven goat's hair for Doug and me: subtle geometric shapes in ochre, tawny orange and chocolate on a creamy background. It's on my bed still. Every time I look at it, I'm reminded of her kindness and her care and the rich voice rising above the clash of bracelets as she gathered Robin and the twins into a last mighty hug after we'd all sat down to tea with Budgie's cream scones.

'You be good kids, eh?' Huge tears coursed down her face to splatter the intricate embroidered bodice of her best robe. 'No nonsense. Uh-uhhhhhh.'

Budgie said as they left, 'There goes an African queen. I feel like a bloody gnat in her presence.'

'A tough gnat, though,' Doug said, and roared. It was the first time in months that he'd cracked a joke.

## 21

Jimbo Lamb erupted into our lives at a riverside pub one Sunday. We were sitting on stools at the bar having pre-lunch drinks when he came up behind Doug and belted him on the shoulder bellowing, 'Percy! Well met by moonlight ha ha.'

With an effort Doug regained his balance and turned. 'Jimbo. How are you?' He was always courteous, even with people he didn't like.

'In the pink. And you? Wee spot of trouble at the moment?'

It was a cruel dig. Bad news got around, despite the fact that they'd not seen each other since Oxford. Doug flushed and said, 'What do you mean?'

'Forced retirement. Happens to the best of us, sport. Never mind, the little woman will provide. Making a name for herself, eh?'

'Indeed. I'm very proud of her.' Barely hanging on to his pride, Doug introduced us but didn't offer him a drink.

Jimbo was a cartoon salesman: loud, brash, presumptuous and fond of his drink. He was the size and shape tailors call portly short, with a red jowly face, chins lapping over his collar and a sharp line in pin-striped suits. He claimed to be a real people person and a terrific success – 'Top of the shots!' – in his chosen field of spirituous liquors. Within minutes he had let us know that they included a rare dark rum from Haiti which he had personally sourced from an elite distillery belonging to a group of Papa Doc's former Tontons Macoutes.

'Bad buggers, but they do the finest rum on God's earth. Cross my heart, all the way down to hell.' He tapped the side of his bulbous nose. 'I move a thousand boxes a year in the UK alone. Angling to get my foot in the door of the US of A under another label this year, make a killing. They won't deal direct with Haiti, you see.'

'Rum, you say?' Doug was interested despite the initial insult.

'It's not Barbancourt, it's better,' Jimbo boasted, naming the island's famous rum. 'More spice, more vanilla, smooth like you wouldn't believe. Try some.' He raised his arm and called to the barmaid, 'Give us three Voodoo Virgins, on the rocks with a slice of lime, darling. And make it snappy.'

I'd already had a glass of wine and was looking forward to another with our lunch. Budgie had changed her day off to be with the children so we could enjoy a quiet meal together, which was looking unlikely unless I got rid of him. I said in a frosty voice, 'Not for me, thanks. We've booked for lunch.'

'Ah! Meeting friends?'

'No,' I said stupidly, 'we were hoping to—'

'Mind if I join you? Haven't seen old Percy in years. I've been meaning to contact him about our college reunion: twenty years after and all that. Got sixteen of the fellows lined up and trying for a full house – no, I tell a lie. Not quite full. Roddy Higgs copped it on the ring road in his MG and Tom Wasimbe was shot in one of those stupid little wars in Africa. Remember him? Fuzzy-wuzzy with the best cover drive you ever saw? He got in a scrap and—'

Jimbo had advanced verbal diarrhoea. We were given a tedious run-down of everyone in their year and told in detail about the process of making his precious rum: 'Pot-stilled from fresh cane juice ... fermented into wine ... aged in oak casks and ...' He expounded on the merits of various grappas pressed on him by Italian winemakers and praised a new liqueur as, 'Heaven with a kick. Best way into women's knickers I know.' Followed by chortling, this time with Doug – well into his second Voodoo Virgin – joining in.

I stuck out the lunch because I didn't want to abandon him. By the end of it, they had flattened five Voodoo Virgins each before I told Jimbo to get lost and drove my sozzled husband home. He sniggered all the way and fell through the front door, coming to rest with his forehead on Budgie's trainers.

She made a joke of it by teasing, 'What's all this now, Boss?'

'Jimbo'sh revenge,' he slurred, struggling to get his tongue round the words. 'The shits shall inherit th' earth.'

'Motherless,' she said to me over his head. 'Who's Jimbo?'

'Someone from college we met in the pub. He's a pig.' I was in a rage. 'Sells what he calls spirituous liquors and made Doug feel so small that he had to compensate by matching him drink for drink.'

'Dangerous porker, then. Mud-wallowing arsehole.' Her sympathy was often unprintable. The children loved it.

We tried to keep Doug's condition from them by hustling him upstairs and into bed, but of course they heard him shouting, 'Let me go, you hushies. Hush puppiesh. Shush huppiesh. Begone!'

They came out of the lounge where they had been draped over the sofas watching TV and stood goggle-eyed at the bottom of the stairs.

'What's wrong with Dad?' Tasha asked.

'You're dragging him,' Chloe pointed out.

'He's drunk.' Robin turned away and stalked back into the lounge, trying not to show how upset he was. Our boy was so like Doug when I'd first met him: the same black hair jutting over his eyes, the same anxious frown, the same urgent will to win that made him do things with twice the intensity of everyone else and keep going twice as long. I ached to see him so disappointed in the father who had been his hero all his life.

Using the excuse of the college reunion, Jimbo kept cropping up in our lives like a florid nightmare. It was only nine months later when the shit hit the fan (Budgie's comment) that I realised he had lain in wait for us at the pub. He needed to recruit a personable man to run the gauntlet of the American liquor industry, still partly Mafia-controlled then, and find chinks where he could sell his illicit rum.

The porker had chosen his victim well. Doug was Oxford-educated with executive experience in the USA, bored with doing nothing, and all too ready to believe in glowing financial prospects that would elevate him to chief breadwinner. Soon Jimbo was telling him (in strictest confidence) about the amazing opportunity that had come up in New York, and offering business-class air tickets, all expenses and a 'very lucrative' commission on sales. All he'd need to do was introduce himself to the liquor middlemen and ensure that the rum was delivered to their warehouses. The first payment would be made the day after delivery.

'Piece of cake, this assignment. You've got it made, sport!' Jimbo brayed, handing him an estimate of the market potential for high-class rum in America. It was a classified secret, but the old boys' network would see Doug right. No man should have to suffer the indignity of being kept by his wife. And he was one of the best, the very best. A topflight chap. Flair second to none. Etcetera, etcetera.

He was not told that Lambéron Genuine Oak-Aged Rum was rotgut and fit only for cooking. The Voodoo Virgins in the pub had been made with mellow twelve-year-old Barbancourt, a cask of which had been bought to fill the sample bottles distributed for tasting. Jimbo kept it in his home cellar along with the capping-and-labelling machine which he later used to doctor bottles filled with poor-quality rum from the Haiti distillery. The scam was for Doug to sell thousands of cases in the United States 'exclusive of excise' (that is, under the counter) which would be simultaneously delivered and paid for COD. Jimbo and the Haitians would then evaporate with their profits, leaving Doug to face the music.

It was a cunning strategy baited to snare a desperate man. And my trustful, honourable, eager husband fell for it.

Elated to be employed again, he bought two new suits, shirts, ties, shoes and a stylish lightweight suitcase with a matching briefcase. And he read up everything he could find about rum and the liquor trade, the cultivation of sugar cane, distilleries, Haiti and import–export regulations.

'I must know what I'm talking about,' he kept saying, alight with the enthusiasm of a new campaign after so many battlefield defeats. He plugged away at the books like a student swotting for his finals, lifting his head only to regale the children and me and Budgie with fascinating snippets about pirates, smugglers, slaves, rum-runners, Prohibition, speakeasies and rum cocktails.

'Fancy.' Budgie wouldn't touch even a glass of wine.

'How can anyone drink that gunk?' Robin was a dedicated Coke fan, scathing about chaps who skived off sports practices to go to pubs and drink, which meant not giving their all to school teams.

'Have you, Dad?' Tasha asked.

'What?'

'Drunk that gunk.'

'Sunk that junk,' Chloe echoed.

They hadn't forgotten that he'd fallen through the front door.

After an uncomfortable pause, Doug said, 'Tried some, of course. It's part of my research, to be knowledgeable about rums. Can't say I like them much.'

'Does that man get them for you?' Chloe demanded.

'Usually. He's my new partner, remember.'

'I hate him. He's so red and fat. Wibbly-wobbly like a jelly.'

'Bibbly-bobbly jelly-belly.'

The twins went off into howls of mocking laughter and even

Budgie cracked a smile. Robin got up and stalked out of the room. I sighed.

Armed with figures about exports of Scotch whisky, Doug went to the United States Information Service in Grosvenor Square and told one of the helpful librarians that he was considering investing in a firm that did a lot of shipping for the liquor trade; could she help with some facts and figures? He came away with a folder full of tables and pie-charts, convinced that he was about to hit the jackpot at last.

'Jimbo's put me on to a good thing,' he enthused that night. 'This is it, Annie. A job where I can be my own man in a guaranteed market. We're selling a quality product that I'm proud to represent.'

'You're a law graduate selling rum,' I pointed out. 'Not commercial property. Not air freight slots. Not pharmaceuticals. Booze.'

'But it's top of the range,' he insisted. 'Think Glenfiddich. Think Moët & Chandon. Think Château Mouton Rothschild. I'm in that league.'

Trying to be glad for him and not negative, I said, 'I truly hope so.' But I was thinking about Jimbo's red face and shifty eyes when we'd met to celebrate Doug's appointment and the signing of a contract.

'I'm off to New York next Monday, then Chicago,' he went on, having clearly waited for the right moment to tell me.

'For how long?'

'Two weeks, probably. It depends on whether I can see all the guys Jimbo has lined up. Could be three if I have to hang around.'

‘Three weeks!’

‘It’s a job, at last. You don’t mind?’ The anxious frown had deepened to permanent vertical grooves.

I gulped down my unease. ‘Of course not, love. I’m glad for you. It’s a real challenge.’

Prophetic words. The real challenge lay in finding a good lawyer to defend him against fraud charges and an extradition order granted in the United States after the scam unfolded. In his favour was the fact that Jimbo had been too stupid to destroy the incriminating barrel of Barbancourt and machinery in his cellar, which ensured his conviction, though the Haiti confederates had vanished. Doug turned state witness and was exonerated with a warning to be more careful in the future. But the disaster left him back at square one: unemployed and more demoralised than ever.

‘Damn and blast the bloody bastards!’ Budgie fulminated.

‘Shit-heads!’ Tasha yelled.

‘Pricks.’ From Chloe.

Even Robin contributed what for him was a precipitous descent into foul language. ‘I always thought that man was a turd. I hope he gets ten years hard fucking labour.’

For once I pretended not to hear. I needed to cuss as much as they did, but let off steam in the shower when I knew Doug was on the river rowing away his rage. It was a very low point in our marriage, made worse by an invitation I received the following month to appear on a New York TV programme about food columnists – with first-class air tickets for me and my husband, a five-star hotel, a generous honorarium and all expenses paid.

Doug refused with a smile as tight as a jerked slipknot. 'Not even you, my darling, could induce me to go back to that place. They wouldn't let me in, anyway.'

'Please,' I begged. 'We could have fun together.'

'Fun? What's that?'

The youthful high flush on his cheekbones had paled to blotches, his eyes were granite, his temples had gone grey. He was a man in deep despair, not waving but drowning. And I was being tempted to leave him and our children to gallivant off for five days of luxury.

I said, 'In that case, I'm not going.'

'Don't be silly. They want you. Enjoy your success.'

'How can I leave when you're so unhappy?'

'Rather one than two of us. You'd resent it eventually and I don't think the kids would like living in a fridge.' The tight smile became mocking. 'Think of it this way, Annie. They've got a resident dad and you have a house-husband.'

I went. New York gave me a few days of relief from the tension and an additional, enthusiastic and very lucrative audience.

*Dear Annie*
*Me again, Our Dawn. You said to beleve in myself and trust my instincs to do the right things but Im not shaw what my instincs are please help.*
*Our Dawn Again*

*Dear Dawn*
*Your instincts are what you really, really know deep inside. Some are automatic reactions, like shutting your eyes against bright*

*lights. Others are things you learn from experience, like picking up a crying child to comfort him and rushing to help someone in danger. Instincts are usually very reliable, so do trust them.*
*Annie*

## 22

The break in New York gave me a fresh perspective on Doug's problems. The Americans I met talked a lot about their faith, meaning religion, and in the plane flying back to London I mulled over these conversations. Faith had a much broader meaning, and I wondered if Doug would become permanently trapped in his slough of insecurity because he had lost all faith in himself. The balance between us had become dangerously lopsided.

I tried to get him to talk about it, but as usual he refused any discussion of his dilemma. 'Back off, Annie. I'm a fuck-up and I have to learn to accept it,' was all he'd say.

'Please, Doug.'

'No.' Followed by some lame excuse like, 'I'm on my way out,' or 'I promised Budgie I'd take the vacuum cleaner to be fixed,' or 'I'm late for my coaching session.' He had volunteered to coach youngsters who joined the rowing club and showed talent. He said often that being on the river was therapeutic and wasn't it a relief to have him out from underfoot for a while?

'You know that's not so,' I'd answer.

'Tell me another.' And he'd be gone for the whole afternoon and sometimes well into the evening, unless Robin's school teams needed transport. He'd bought the Ford station wagon when the drug company closed down the UK branch. Besides its cavernous interior, there was a roof-rack that could carry two four-man rowing shells and their oars. Budgie and I continued to use the old Vauxhall from our Chiswick days when life had been so rosy and full of promise.

Mum and Dad were now spending every summer in the garden flat down the road. I was their only chicken, Mum said, and they wanted to know their grandchildren. I tried to talk to her about Doug, but it was hard to pin her down before the conversation veered off to painting. She was working at it full-time now.

Paintings were propped against the walls of an extra bedroom two and three deep: mostly figure studies (including women, I was relieved to see) and portraits, though she'd been on painting holidays in Italy and the resultant landscapes were much praised. Several were hanging in a Richmond gallery and on my fortieth birthday she had given me a view of Ravenna which I loved.

'Mum, I need your advice,' I whined in the umpteenth attempt to get her full attention.

We were sitting on the sofa looking out into the garden. Dad had gone off fishing in Scotland, though often in the afternoons he'd be on the river with Robin, having bought a small boat with an outboard engine. His only criticism of Mum nowadays was that she stank of oil paints and wouldn't cook his trout. She'd reply that he stank of fish, so what? Both had never looked happier.

She feigned elaborate shock at the very idea of my needing her advice. 'This is a first. I thought you were the guru who knew everything.'

'Don't be like that. I really need your help. Doug's sliding into depression again. The kids are so worried.'

'And you?' She gave me her familiar over-the-specs look.

'Miserable. He's changed so much. Everything gets twisted. He says our lives are an interminable contest with me winning all the races and getting all the medals. It's really stupid.' I dissolved into angry tears.

Mum moved closer and put her arm round my shoulders. 'Buck up, love. He's had a tough time.'

'I know *that*. I just don't know how to help him,' I sobbed.

'You can't, beyond love and understanding. He needs to help himself.'

I hauled some tissues out of my bag and tried to stop crying. It was vital to be coherent to keep Mum's one-track mind focused on my problem. 'I'm *being* loving and sympathetic and supportive, telling him it doesn't matter, to keep looking and he'll find the right job. But since the Jimbo disaster he sees himself as a hopeless failure. What more can I do?'

'Be more aware of how you sound,' she said.

'What do you mean?'

'You're so pleased with yourself, Annie. Verging on smug, if I must be honest. And that's hard for any partner to live with, let alone a man whose working life keeps falling apart. It took me a long time to find my way past being a fifties housewife and the mother of a conspicuously successful daughter. Doug needs encouragement of the efforts he makes, not continual offers of help.'

I was outraged. 'But I never, ever thought of you as a housewife! It's not my fault that you feel that way. And I do encourage Doug's efforts. I do.' The tears began again, a rainstorm I couldn't stop.

Mum got up saying, 'I can't talk if you go on like that. Get a grip on yourself while I make some tea.'

As she scuffled round in the kitchen, I fished out another wad of tissues and pressed them over my eyes to stem the flow. Here I was past forty, and blubbing like a child. Thank goodness the twins weren't around to see it.

When Mum came back with a tray, I was a sodden heap of silent misery. She said, 'That's better. Milk and sugar?'

'Just milk.' I wasn't going to make this easy for her.

The business with cups and saucers and milk-jug and teapot over, she turned to me. 'Annie. How can I put this? You seem impervious to the fact that successful people, however kind and loving, get up the noses of friends and partners – and mothers – who are struggling to make their way. It begins to feel like a gross injustice if you believe you're also talented, and this sense of unfairness can corrode the most amiable relationship.'

'So it's my fault? I'm a smug bitch who wallows in her own glory and is insensitive to the people she loves, is that it?'

'No, dear. What I'm saying is that success can be a bubble isolating you from reality. As I was by the constraints of my time: being a wife and mother who strove to live up to the norms my friends lived by, instead of following my own path. I tried to fit into the herd when I should have been galloping up the nearest hill to check out the view on the other side.'

It was a revelation: she had described a lone ranger, which is how I saw myself. We weren't so different after all. I said, 'What made you leave the herd?'

'My lack of purpose. After you left home, I got bored with holding dinners and the charity work and political protests. I didn't have an exciting career like yours, but I'm no dimwit either. So I looked at various alternatives and joined a painting class. I wanted to do something for *me*. And it's become my passion.'

'That's so selfish.' I'd always thought of her as having the white South African madam's social conscience that operated during the hours when it suited her and closed down when inconvenient.

She gave me a sardonic look. 'You should know.'

I ignored the innuendo. 'When did you get so serious about painting?'

'Far too late. Doug's in a similar situation. He went into business without giving a thought to other careers, and now he can't find his way out.'

'Are you saying he's not good enough to be an executive?'

'No, dear,' she repeated. 'You're not listening to me. I'm saying that he needs time and breathing space to figure out what has happened to him and why, then to consider his options – going back to law, or taking an aptitude test that could lead him in a new direction. What he doesn't need from you are helpful suggestions and pity.'

'I don't pity him.' But I did, I realised. I'd begun to think he wasn't coping because of some innate character flaw.

'Just let him recover on his own, Annie. He's a very bright, very capable man who's lost his bearings. He'll work things out. Believe me.'

'Wish I could believe you. It's hard living with someone you feel you can't get through to any more.'

Tears were welling again, but her next question quelled them. 'Do you still sleep together?'

'That's none of your business.'

'Maybe not. But it helps enormously if you're connecting on a physical level. Dad and I –' she hesitated, then went on, '– well, we still enjoy a bit of rumpty-tumpty. It's what keeps us together.'

'Mum!' I didn't want to hear this.

She grinned. 'Why are you so shocked? Older people have sexual needs too. I'm quite hot in bed now. Painting turns me on. Dad's delighted.'

Hell, this was all I needed: my mother the relentless sex maniac, unhinged by the sight of the well-hung male nudes who posed for her classes. I wondered if all the other participants were older women copping an eyeful to improve their sex lives. And how did the guys feel, sitting there starkers to be ogled by grannies with their minds on one thing.

The thought produced a reluctant laugh, then Mum laughed too and I went away feeling better, vowing to do my best to let Doug be.

The conversation also gave me an idea for my next handbook: *Faith & Faithfulness* by 'Mary Goodman' – a surprising hit for the publisher, who had been anxious about its secular approach. Over sixty thousand copies were sold and the royalties took care of half the remaining mortgage. I didn't have the courage to tell Doug, though. On the blackest of those dark days, he had said that I made him feel emasculated.

*Dear Annie*
*This year is our golden wedding but my old man still wants me on the bed morning, noon and night, and I'm sick and tired of it. Not to mention sore. I always thought he'd calm down when he got to seventy, but he says it's his right and maybe his John Thomas won't be up to the job soon. It's more like his electric eel if you ask me. Should I put tranquillisers in his tea?*
*Winsome*

*Dear Winsome*
*Incompatible sexual needs are one of the problem areas of marriage. However, tampering with your husband's tea is a no-no. I suggest that you consult a counsellor or better still, a sex therapist. Women have rights too!*
*Annie*

I had to resist a powerful urge to call him 'the old goat'.

My booklet *Faith & Faithfulness* took the usual upbeat approach – advise people how to improve themselves, and assure them that they can. It began:

***Introduction***

*In recent years the word 'faith' has become entangled in the public mind with religion, but it has a much wider sense. Having faith doesn't only mean believing in God. At the very least, you should have faith in yourself, in friends and family, the power of good, and the future.*

*Faith is grounded in trust and optimism; it is a fact that people are strengthened and motivated by firmly held beliefs,* whatever they are.

*Doctors and researchers in many parts of the world are studying the healing power of faith and meditation under laboratory conditions ...*

Motivational literature is big on sage advice and checklists, and by now I could churn them out almost in my sleep.

*Faith & Faithfulness* wasn't universally acclaimed. Angry pastors attacked it from the pulpit, saying that it was blasphemy – which gave it wider publicity.

My publisher received an avalanche of fan mail from readers who had been heartened by its straightforward message: follow your deeply-held beliefs and you'll be a stronger person.

If only I had believed what I wrote. My faith in Doug was under severe strain.

## 23

Robin was heading for seventeen that difficult year, and the twins fourteen – all with distinctive personalities and the usual teenage problems.

Robin was in that classic hiatus between giving his all for his school teams, and the realisation that girls were diverting his thoughts from more serious matters like exams and captain duties. He abandoned his Rubik's Cube and BMX bike and became particular about his clothes: denim jeans had to be just so, sweatshirts large but not baggy, T-shirts to have relevant logos. When the twins begged to be taken to *Dirty Dancing*, he went off with his best mate to see *The Last Emperor* one Saturday afternoon, having heard that someone's sister would be at the same performance with her friends.

He came home two hours later than promised, saying, 'Sorry. We had coffee afterwards.' Coffee! It had been milkshakes in the healthy-eating-for-super-fitness phase that followed his hamburger and Coke period.

Navigating the choppy seas between manly pursuits and girls' concerns was made easier by having sisters, though he missed his former closeness to Doug who was out most afternoons. The old Austin 6 sat half-stripped and covered in dust in its stall in the coach house with the engine parts tumbled into a tin trunk. 'He doesn't have time for me any more,' Robin said more than once.

Tasha and Chloe did their best to fill in for their father's absence by being animated and amusing – 'The life and soul,' Budgie called them, adding, 'Good thing somebody's cheerful around here. Turning into a bloody morgue with the Boss so down in the dumps.'

I suspect that she had begun calling Doug 'the Boss' to counter his prevailing grievance. 'Busy as a bee, our Annie,' I'd heard him say to her in the kitchen. 'Needs a drone like me to provide contrast.'

'You're not a drone, Boss,' Budgie had said. 'More like a wasp: good-looking bugger with a nasty sting in your tail.'

His sudden laugh had been an infrequent sound. When he wasn't out rowing or coaching, he'd be in the attic banging up partition walls and a ceiling at one end. He told everyone it was going to be his study, adding, 'I need a space I can call my own that isn't infested with busyness.'

Robin and the twins took the hint and kept away. I was just relieved that Doug hadn't said more. We were still sleeping in the same bed and there were nights when we made love, though I was left feeling obscurely guilty afterwards.

But usually we went to bed at different times and if one read, the other would pretend to sleep. I kept my tears for the times when he was out. If he noticed that my eyes were red and swollen, he didn't ask why.

Budgie sympathised with trays of tea, cursing the demi-gods of capitalism.

'A pox on the greedy swine! May they rot in their dark satanic mills.'

'It isn't the mills,' I said. 'It's the offices where duels are fought in immaculate shirts with gold cufflinks. Doug was shafted by Baz Fuller because he wasn't ruthless enough. He's too nice.'

'Fuck that!' Budgie exploded. 'Why do you think I left MI6? Not because I was too nice. I'm not. Or because a randy arsehole shoved his hand up my skirt. I could have kicked him in the balls. Put him out of action like *that*.' She snapped fingers that looked like twigs but had the strength of high-tensile steel. 'Sexual silly buggers was a useful excuse. I had to get out. Couldn't take the power games. The naked bloody ambition. The Boss is the same.'

'He's beginning to think he's unemployable.'

'Just needs to find a hole he fits into,' Budgie said, with all the confidence I lacked. Adding, 'As the bishop said to the actress.'

'The nakedly ambitious bishop, I presume?'

She let out a hoot like Euphemia's and we both felt better. There wasn't much to laugh about that year.

Robin was at an all-boys school. The twins had chosen Whitegables, a progressive school twenty minutes' drive from the house where they could pursue their interests: Tasha in the gym and workshop, Chloe in the science laboratory and school gardens. Although they were close and always echoing each other, their temperaments couldn't have been more different.

Tasha, the eldest by seven minutes, was all action and an outrageous show-off, but also a great reader and good with her hands. The Whitegables ethos held that creating things was as important as academics and outdoor activities, and there were classes in painting, pottery, sculpture, woodwork and horticulture. Tasha chose wood carving and moved on to making small boxes with marquetry inlays. Extreme contrast was her nature: the hectic girl flying out above the river or soaring over a bar doing high jumps could give way within the hour to an intent craftswoman cutting shapes out of wood veneers with a sharp craft knife and steady hands.

Chloe adored all living things, from flowers to insects to animals, and from an early age wanted to be a biologist. Her childhood fascination with mice and guinea pigs had given way to horse worship at the stables which took all her spare time.

At school she concentrated on science subjects and worked with the head gardener, a horticulture graduate who stomped about doing experiments like cross-fertilising stamens with earbuds to create new hybrids. She'd bring seedlings home for Budgie's vegetable garden or appear in my study with a bunch of flowers and a big smile, saying, 'For you, Mum. I grew them.'

Chloe's stubborn, persistent, curious nature made her good at research, though she found it impossible to put insects into killing jars and pin out pathetic little frog corpses on dissecting boards. Dad showed her how to kill fish by giving them a sharp blow on the head with a priest, explaining, 'It's instantaneous. No suffering.' But Chloe was adamant: she'd ask her friends or Tasha to do the deed and pin out her subjects, then wait until they were cold before tackling them.

'Queasy Chloe,' Tasha called her.

'And you're Tasha the Dasher.'

'Beamish squeam.'

'Smashing Tash.'

'Oh, shut *up*!' Robin would groan as they went on trading silly words. He was studying for his O levels and trying not to mind that his father didn't show any interest in his progress.

*Dear Annie*
*My Dad hates me. He keeps saying that I might think I'm smart and hot stuff but I'll never get a man. What he never says is I'm fat. It's like, he's slagging off the wrong things, you know? So I just stand there making double chins and looking thick, which makes him hopping mad. I call it my village idiot strategy ha ha.*
*Hayley*

*Dear Hayley*
*You are clearly not a village idiot, so have you considered that your father is trying to tell you in his oblique male way that you could try and lose weight? I think this would be a much better strategy. Look in your phone book for the nearest Weight-Watchers and phone for a consultation. You have nothing to lose but those chins.*
*Annie*

My friends were a great comfort at this time. Susie had become a mother working from home as I did, and brought her baby daughter in a carry-cot to join our cooking sessions. After Zeke had taken the photographs and gone off in his usual hurry to get to his next assignment, we'd sit down with Budgie and chat over the meal we'd cooked. Susie regaled us with gossip about her mother's upper-crust friends and Xavier's clients, I talked about Lally and the kids and sometimes Doug, and Budgie gave us the benefit of her experience with men, replete with four-letter words.

'You mustn't worry about the Boss,' she'd say. 'He just needs time. Blokes act like effing salted snails when their egos are bruised. Curl up and froth.'

'It's such acid froth.'

'I know,' Susie said. 'You'd think the heavens had fallen if a client doesn't like one of Xavier's designs. They're bound up with his manhood somehow.'

'That's just it. Doug keeps saying I make him feel emasculated.'

'Testosterone!' Budgie banged the table. 'Bloody stuff dwindles when there's a crisis. Cocks won't perform. Blokes get a fright and blame it on who? The girlfriend. The wife. Tight underpants. Female hormones in the water. Bollocks! Shall I tell you rule number one for women who work with men? Don't joke about sex. Their biggest fear is that Willy won't sit up and beg on demand.'

Susie and I laughed till we cried. Budgie understood what we were going through and I wondered about her emotional life as a spirited single woman. Had there been affairs with fellow spies – trysts in smoky bars and mist-wreathed alleys, hats pulled down to shadow their faces, endearments muttered in low voices? Or had she fought men off, our Amazon housekeeper with the stature and face of a wizened elf?

Susie was now an official researcher for *Modern Lifestyle* and began to widen her scope from cooking to the serious subjects I never found time for any more.

Lally had her working on articles about financial planning and interior design when other magazines were still dithering on about household budgets and wallpapering the nursery.

Remembering Susie and Budgie's stalwart support at that difficult time, I think real sisters couldn't have been more loving or helpful.

Vron and Cuckoo and I, the survivors of the Fearsome Foursome, had been drawn together by our mutual horror over Jude's murder and met sometimes at a coffee shop or a pub in Chiswick when Vron and Cuckoo could get away from work and I had a few hours to spare.

Neither had children so we talked about Jude, old times, work and men. Vron had grown brittle and censorious, though Cuckoo was her usual self. Matured into a humorous high-care specialist, she still dropped by our home every few months to gossip and laugh, mainly about the clumsy doctors who handled her babies, 'With gauntlets instead of kid gloves.'

There was always a point in our survivors' conversation when one said, 'You're so lucky to have Doug, Annie,' and the other would say something like, 'Good men are hard enough to find, let alone keep.' They knew Doug and I were having problems though I didn't enlarge on the details, not wanting to be disloyal or rub in their single status.

Old friends can be really dense about each other.

## 24

We hadn't celebrated our birthdays during Doug's tribulations, so when Lally said she'd give me fifty pounds to create an exciting birthday buffet, I answered cautiously. 'What did you have in mind?' Her idea of exciting wasn't mine.

'Can you out-do the opposition without going overboard?' she demanded. 'I want something simple but spectacular.'

'It's hard to do spectacular on fifty quid.'

She snapped, 'Inexpensive style has always been our byword. Better look to your laurels, darling. All the cooks bursting into print are professionally trained. I don't want *Fabulous Food* falling behind.' Her receiver crashed down.

The opposition was now very stiff indeed. Prue Leith had followed up her restaurant and school with *Leith's Cookery Course* in three sections. Martha Stewart, doyenne of American homemakers, had published her lavishly illustrated *Entertaining* in 1982. Arabella Boxer, the *Sunday Times* cookery editor, had produced a magnum opus in 1983: her sumptuous *Sunday Times Complete Cook Book* with special-occasion menus by eight famous cooks at the back. She had written in her introduction,

'Into it I have poured all my enthusiasms and prejudices: my love for food, and for cooking, in all its traditional forms, and my growing irritation with phoney and unrealistic trends ... Foreign exotics such as tempura and bourride are fun as occasional variations, but they should be seen against a solid background.'

I was a journalist upstart with no culinary training who'd been successful because I'd managed to capture the spirit of my times. I couldn't compete with the experts. All I had going for me were a gut feeling for what readers needed, a talent for making inexpensive entertaining appear effortless, Zeke's magnificent photographs and my faithful *Modern Lifestyle* fans.

Many of them had grown up with me, metamorphosing from young wives to women who had to juggle husbands, kids, homes and careers. Family life had changed almost out of recognition. Where going out to a restaurant had been an occasional treat, working couples who couldn't be bothered to cook every night relied on cafés, delis and supermarkets at the end of the day. Disillusion with frozen meals and fast foods meant that when they got around to cooking, people were particular about ingredients like freshly made pasta.

Bogged down by their multiple problems, more readers than ever wrote begging for advice and help. Some were struggling with such awful predicaments that Quince often advised me to call in social services or even the police for expert assistance. Suicidal teenagers were a nightmare and needed careful tracking down so I wasn't revealed as the source of privileged information.

I also had help from an unexpected source. Budgie was a whiz when it came to finding people or winkling out personal details, admitting that she had maintained an unofficial network of contacts created in her MI6 days. When I joked that she must have a little black book, she brushed me off with a brisk, 'Don't even go there. I'd have to kill you if I told you.'

*Dear Annie*
*My mum only told me yesterday that my dad didn't die like she always said. She was raped in the park one night by someone whose face she never saw, then he stabbed her and ran away leaving her for dead. She had to crawl two blocks for help leaving a trail of blood. Oh God, why did she have me? Who am I, hers or his? Does this mean I'm tainted?*
*Shelley (not my real name)*

*Dear Shelley*
*No child is born tainted, and your mum must be very brave and love you very much to have kept you and brought you up. Be proud of having such a courageous mother and being who you are: hers.*
*Annie*

My dilemma with Lally's expectations for *Fabulous Food* was that I often included the 'foreign exotics' that the haute cuisine-trained chefs of the seventies and eighties perceived as ethnic oddities. Having been brought up on meat and three veg, I thought carpaccio and tabbouleh and stir-fries were delicious. I scoured friends' and library cookbooks for more unusual recipes from abroad that could be made quickly with available ingredients, yet taste 'different' and show flair. Never having had to make béarnaise sauce by hand or torture vegetables into julienne strips or learn the precise difference between a pâté, a galantine and a terrine, I ignored classic methods as long as the end result was good. No, better than good: terrific.

But Lally's warning about falling behind gave me a fright. We'd be in trouble if she terminated my contracts with *Modern Lifestyle*. The motivational books alone wouldn't earn enough to keep us all going while Doug remained unemployed.

For the buffet party, she wanted brilliant on a shoestring and I had to come up with the goods. Doug growled that it was a dumb idea to pretend it was for a birthday and left the house during the discussions and preparations. To compound my problem, Susie had gone to Holland with Xavier to show off their new baby to his parents, though she helped to plan the feast.

'Lally wants spectacular but not too complicated,' I explained. 'The limit's fifty quid.'

Susie laughed and said, 'The moon, as usual. You'll have to be creative about donated ingredients,' before suggesting possible contributors.

That buffet was a triumph of ingenuity, hard work, Zeke's photography, Budgie's fresh vegetables, Chloe's flowers, the twins' artistic arrangements – and my cheating.

I pestered Dad for free smoked salmon from a fishing friend's smoker and Mum for the jars of olives, artichoke hearts and anchovy fillets on her kitchen shelf. I weaselled some cheeses out of a delicatessen and a selection of breads from our local bakery, promising to name them in the article. I used staples from my kitchen, eggs from a woman down the road who kept hens, and raspberries from a neighbour's garden. Only the meat, the cream and the wines were paid for out of the fifty pounds, which meant we could splurge on far more champagne than was mentioned in the article.

And I massaged the expenses by announcing that friends had brought some of the dishes as birthday gifts for the feast in two parts.

The first part, laid out on one of Euphemia's jazzy Ghanaian cotton bedspreads with a rainbow of zinnias and trailing ivy, were crudités (baby carrots, young radishes and green beans, mange-touts, courgette and celery sticks, spring onions, strips of green and red peppers, blanched asparagus, cherry tomatoes, quartered mushrooms) with three dips: garlic mayonnaise, sour cream and avocado; antipasto (Parma ham, salami, anchovy fillets, artichoke hearts and black Calamata olives); smoked salmon on brown bread and butter triangles; a carving board piled with slices of cold roast lamb, with mint and redcurrant sauces on the side; and French baguettes, onion and herb breads.

The desserts were served in a riot of nasturtiums on the scrubbed kitchen table: fresh raspberries and cream; trifle (Budgie's sherry-laden recipe) and a cheese board with savoury biscuits.

Everybody loved it and we all ate ourselves silly after Zeke had finished with his photographs, including a sequence of my opening some presents. Readers loved the personal angle.

My best present was Doug, who had complained about his space being invaded and scoffed at the idea of a pretend birthday buffet. But he appeared minutes before our first guest and seemed like his old self opening the wine, pouring drinks, chatting up the women and later helping Budgie, Robin, the twins and me with the clearing up and dish-washing.

'Thanks,' I said gratefully as we leant against the back door for air after Budgie had hung up the last damp dishcloth and the children had trailed upstairs to bed. 'I thought you weren't going to come.'

He turned to look at me. 'I didn't want to let you down, surprise surprise.' The frown had settled back between his eyes.

'Did you enjoy yourself?'

'Mostly. I'm not a complete spoilsport yet.'

'Course not. You're my rock.' I slipped my arm round his waist but instead of leaning into me, he stiffened.

'Rock. Just squatting here.'

I turned to face him, trying to stop the rot before it escalated. 'Don't, Doug. It's been a great evening in our beautiful home—'

'Which I just hang around. Face the facts, Annie,' he said. 'I'm redundant.'

'Can't you stop harping on about it?' I blurted. 'It's hard living with someone who keeps running himself down and hiding away in case he gets hurt again. We love you and want you back. All of us. I do, desperately.'

'So desperately that you don't mind supporting a drone?'

His unremitting self-pity was too much at the end of that lovely evening. I shouted, 'Of course I don't bloody mind! I've always believed we were a team, not in competition. And you're not a drone, you're a gutless moaning Minnie.'

He drawled, 'Ah, the truth at last. Allow me to reciprocate. You dash off your impressive meals with such ease, Annie. This so-called birthday feast was a con, but your faithful readers will pester Lally begging for more. You think it's hard living with me? Let me tell you that it's fucking torture living with someone who's turning my family life into a three-ring circus. As an agony aunt – or should I say sob sister? – you ought to be the first to understand.'

The truth. Violent thugs had murdered Jude, but what had killed the dream that had been Our Song? I looked at my husband's face seething with accusation and remembered a line from the second verse, about being alone and blue. With the chasm deepening between us, there were no more words to be said that night. He slept in the spare room. I lay awake for hours in our empty double bed feeling the chill of his defeat, then cried myself to sleep. Judging by the swollen eyes at breakfast next morning, so did everyone else.

As Doug had predicted, my faithful readers loved the feast. There were hundreds of letters to the editor asking for more ideas from Annie Butterfield about luxurious meals created on a budget.

'You swindled them and me,' Lally barked when she phoned to tell me. 'Don't gyppo the cost again, or you're fired.' I crossed my fingers as she forged on. 'Better change tack for a few months. I want family favourites. Things my mother or granny taught me. Peasant dishes. Casseroles. Pot-au-feu. Authentic from-the-heart cooking, not food fraud. Okay?'

'Okay.' I didn't have any fight left.

# 25

My enthusiastic amateur's approach was scorned by professional cooks and counsellors, yet lapped up by *Modern Lifestyle* readers for nearly twenty years until Annie Butterfield and her homely kitchen and old-fashioned advice began to sound as quaint as the mad hatter tea parties beloved of the Women's Institute.

But this was still 1987 and I had an unemployed, depressed, angry husband who was slipping away from me and our family. His disappointments had slowed him from the self-assured man I'd married to a watchfulness that crackled with tension. Now Robin was at an age when he needed help from his father – advice about sport and girls, for starters – which wasn't forthcoming.

Budgie and I tried to fill the gaps. My worry was compounded by the letters I received from single mothers with troubled daughters whose problems seemed to have begun in their early teens when their fathers died or disappeared. Quince said once, 'It's a time when girls need their fathers' approval to help them develop into confident women who form lasting relationships. A caring adult male can substitute for a father, but to have a loving, supportive dad and mum in a close marriage is the best start for a girl.'

Doug had been a loving, supportive dad from the moment of Robin's birth, and I'd been lucky with my Dad who was fond and proud of me. My parents' marriage had seemed unremarkable but they appeared to be enjoying the renewed rumpty-tumpty: there were times when Mum looked like the cat that licked the cream. By contrast, my once-close marriage was showing danger signs that affected the twins. I'd always thought that daredevil Tasha and stubborn Chloe were as outgoing as I had been as a teenager, but now they turned to each other for company and stopped bringing friends home.

I poured out my worries to Quince, asking what more I could do for Doug. 'Should I encourage him to keep applying for jobs, which makes him more resentful, or should I just cross my fingers and hope he sees reason?'

'Can't you think of a more positive tactic without pissing him off completely?' Like Budgie, she didn't mince her words.

'I don't know any,' I admitted. 'The fact is that he hates me being what he calls "the essential breadwinner". His pride has taken such a knock that I don't think it can ever recover.'

'And deep down, he feels it's grossly unfair because his abilities and experience are as good as yours, if not better?'

I nodded. She had it exactly. Doug had grown up in the fifties when men ruled the roost. He believed he was hard done by instead of trying to analyse why things had gone so wrong.

'Try writing about the situation as though you're responding to a reader,' Quince suggested. 'Able women always have problems with men who are less successful. We continually have to fish the silly arses out of trouble, dry them out and prop them up.'

She was talking from experience, I realised. 'You too?'

'Me too. But I carry an extra millstone: he's a lovable alcoholic and far gone now, though I won't give up on him. Be grateful that Doug is fit, keeps busy rowing and coaching, and doesn't hit the bottle. Hang in there, Annie.'

'I'll try,' I said, humbled by her infinitely worse circumstances.

That conversation led to a column that produced a flood of grateful letters and another 'Well done, you' from Lally.

'Life is a strange beast,' she added. 'When they appointed me women's page editor on the paper all those years ago, I was told not to expect further promotion. The editors on Fleet Street were all men. Now I'm the brains behind the world's most successful family magazine, male editors bow and scrape. I showed 'em.'

'You'd never have got married like I did.'

'Not to a *man*. Una and I are kindred souls. Beyond capable and no time for fools.' Ten years later they went through a formal and very public ceremony of commitment, to general praise from the media.

I tailored my column carefully, well aware that Doug would recognise himself if he saw it – though he seldom read my work. 'Women's stuff,' he called it.

***Annie Butterfield Advises***
*A reader has written to ask: how can I turn my unsatisfactory life around and start anew?*

*Most people take a wrong direction at some time. Often you get so daunted by the circumstances that it seems impossible to move on. The consequent depression feeds on itself, sapping your will and your energy, generating nagging doubts that hinder everything you try to do. Life has become shades of grey.*

*But try not to give in to despair, however tempting …*

I gave it four hundred words of inspirational gung-ho, ending with:

***Annie advises:*** *Nothing is impossible. Repeat, nothing is impossible. Try to assess what went wrong and why (get professional help if necessary), aim for a new direction that interests you, and take regular small steps towards it. Explorers like Amundsen and Scott made it to the South Pole by trudging on, one foot in front of the other, following a compass. You too can do it.*

Lally phoned to tell me she'd received the biggest mailbag in months from readers about their appallingly unsatisfactory lives, all desperate for ideas on how to turn them around.

It was a shock when she went on, 'Great response, but the column was much too vague. Two obsessed male rivals plodding about the icy wastes at the turn of the century are hardly role models for today's women. You're losing your touch, Annie.'

I was used to her tactic of sudden accusation and said, 'Come off it. The response proves that I was on the button.'

'The responders are asking for more, not marvelling at your amazing perspicacity. They want concrete solutions. It's not enough to expound on problems, you've got to offer remedies.'

'I did! Find a new direction and head for it.'

'That's too easy. A cop-out. You're the agony aunt with the answers. That pathetic husband of yours must be taking more of a toll than I thought.'

'Of course he isn't,' I bleated. 'I'm fine.'

'You'd better be. I want more specific advice, okay? Ask Pat Quincey if you run out of ideas.' Just before the phone slammed down, she repeated, 'More specific. Or else.'

Or else. She was threatening me. I tried harder.

*Dear Annie*
*I'm in a right pickle: two months pregnant and my boyfriend yells at me to get lost, it can't be his. The creep. I don't want to be stuck with a kid, especially not his. Where can I get proper help? I'm scared of going round the corner and my mum will kill me if she finds out.*
*Mad As A Snake*

*Dear Mad (I'd be too, in your position)*
*You've put me in a pickle because this magazine is unable for legal reasons to detail possible solutions. But you are quite right to be scared of going round the corner. Your best bet is a Marie Stopes Clinic or the gynaecology outpatients at a big hospital*

*where the nursing staff will give you advice in strict confidence.*
*Annie*

Most of the letters about unwanted pregnancies had no address. If there was one, I wrote a note giving directions to the nearest clinic or gynae outpatients. It was the only counsel I could give.

Their GPs were likely to be formidable men in suits and ties who shrank from sexual predicaments. And even though savvy women knew they could have an abortion with a discreet D&C, we couldn't say that in a family magazine. The next writer could have been the answer for Mad As A Snake, but I had no way of connecting them.

*Dear Annie*
*I want a baby but I'm never gunna marry – can't do with men's nonsense. Maybe I could adopt one? There must be a kid out there what needs a loving mum.*
*Doris*

*Dear Doris*
*There are millions of children who need a loving mum, but sadly adoption societies don't consider unmarried parents unless there are exceptional circumstances. In the meantime, if you're serious, a private adoption is possible, though there are stringent legal conditions. Send me a stamped, self-addressed envelope if you'd like to pursue this option.*
*Annie*

Warm-hearted Cuckoo had arranged a number of private adoptions, linking women who couldn't conceive or carry babies to term with mothers looking for people to adopt their babies. She had moved to a smaller maternity hospital in Kent where the matron made allowances for exceptional circumstances.

'That's better, Annie. Solutions, not diatribes,' Lally commented when she'd read these replies.

But the writing was on the wall.

# 26

No thanks to my column about starting afresh, there were good times coming after the doldrums of 1987, though they meant a seismic change in our lives.

Out of the blue Doug met an old friend from Oxford who was competing in the single sculls event at the rowing club, Alex Wetherby. They had belonged to a group of earnest students who'd debated points of law over their pints in the Eagle and Child and played squash and rowed together. In the self-conscious way of aspiring intellectuals, brave new ideas had been tossed around like confetti. They'd worn suede jackets and narrow scarves and smoked thin cigars, and been dismissive of contact sports like rugby, which they'd said were for overgrown schoolboys. Occasionally I'd been allowed to join them.

After their cooling-down chat over beers on the rowing club terrace, Doug asked him home for supper and called me, saying, 'Remember Alex Wetherby at Oxford? He's in the Foreign Office now. I've just been rowing with him and want to bring him home for supper.'

'Of course I remember Alex.'

Especially the discussion on the influence of given names over people's characters, when he'd said that his parents must have looked deep into a crystal ball when they named him Alexander, and I couldn't understand why. As a common journalist working for a living then, I'd kept quiet at those gatherings for fear of being inconsequential.

I went on, 'I'd love to see him again.'

Doug was in hyper-anxious mode. 'I'd like to impress him. We should be there around seven-thirty. Can you and Budgie and the kids pull out all the stops?'

'You want an impressive meal at an hour's notice?'

'Just make some of your fabulous fast food. For me this time, not Lally.'

'A compliment. Wonders will never cease.'

'Don't be like that tonight,' he pleaded. 'Alex was a good friend. He gave us our most memorable wedding present: those avant-garde aluminium ashtrays, a Danish design. We swanked about them to everyone.'

I had to laugh. 'When everyone smoked.'

His answering chuckle was a rare sound that year. 'Alex still does. You'd better dig them out, plus some decent wine. And ask the kids to be on their best behaviour. I want him to see a happy family, not an ongoing skirmish.'

How had we got to this edgy stand-off after our loving years together? 'We're all desperate to be a happy family again, Doug,' I said.

There was a pause, then he stuttered, 'I – I'm sorry I'm such a useless husband. And father.'

'That's not true. We just want the old you back.'

'Silly bugger got waylaid.' The phone went down, abrupt as a full stop.

Keen to please him, the team swung into action. Budgie and I whistled round the kitchen making a chocolate and orange mousse, baking potatoes, putting a salad together and preparing steaks to be grilled at the last minute. Robin organised the wine and the glasses. The twins laid a festive table featuring Chloe's arrangement of field flowers.

Alex won her heart by saying they were exquisite and requesting one for his buttonhole. He praised Tasha's wooden boxes and said her inlay designs were elegant and well executed. He discussed movies and cricket with Robin, joked about the Oxford days with Doug, complimented me on my success as a media icon and the best meal he'd had in months, and disappeared into the kitchen afterwards to gossip with Budgie about recent intrigues in MI6. Doug must have informed him because she was usually tight-lipped about her past – though all her defences tumbled when Alex came.

It's funny how lives change. Dauntingly bright and charming Alex had gone into the diplomatic corps expecting to become an ambassador. Many postings and disappointments later, he had taken the hint that gay men were non grata if they didn't marry, and came home to a high-ranking but mundane government job. Doug the resolute striver, also bright and charming, was serially unemployed. And the common journalist who'd been too awed to speak in their presence had become famous and was supporting her family thanks to her columns and books – arms-length wisdom maybe, but lucrative.

As Lally had said of life, fate is a strange beast. My comeuppance in a few years' time would be as unexpected as it was cruel.

Alex came visiting often after that evening, saying he'd always wanted to be an uncle, and would the kids oblige?

What a question. They adored his stories about the countries he'd served in and diplomatic debacles. Doug relaxed into his old self and we both enjoyed the pleasures of intelligent conversation and fascinating insights into the ways governments operate.

After several months he confided late one night as the three of us sat over a last glass of wine that he and his long-standing partner had split up when he left the diplomatic corps.

'Geoffrey wants to be an ambassador so badly that he decided to marry. His wife knows about us; her trade-off is children and the good life at the top.'

'That's awful for all three of you.'

'Annie! How can you say that?' Doug was furious.

'She's right.' Alex regarded his immaculate fingernails. 'It is awful. I lost the love of my life, Geoffrey has lost his self-respect, and the nice woman he's married will suffer.' He gave us a painful smile.

'I'm consoling myself with a radical scheme for my early retirement from the Foreign Office next year: I'm buying a home on a new golf estate in the Winelands near Cape Town called Rigby Vale. It's relatively cheap now because of the worsening trouble in South Africa, but I hear on the grapevine that your government is considering releasing Nelson Mandela.'

'Not *our* government,' Doug and I both said. We'd lived in England for over twenty years. We were English now. Our children were English.

'Let me finish. I hear that he's a remarkable man who will save your country from itself. Bishop Desmond Tutu said so in a recent speech, and I believe him. So I'm giving it a go. I need to get away from this smug little island and its even more smug bureaucrats.'

'But we'll lose you,' I blurted.

'Not yet. It'll be six months before the house is ready.'

Doug said, 'Didn't know you played golf?'

'I like the game and play to a reasonable handicap. It's a useful skill for diplomats, ingratiates us with politicians and businessmen. Golfers gossip, you know? And there's another plus to up-market estates: presentable single men are always in demand. You'd be surprised what confidences are murmured in my ear over cocktails.'

I said, 'Being an agony aunt means never having to say you're surprised.'

He laughed and turned to Doug. 'What about the agony uncle? You've been through the mill too. Both of us were such promising students.'

'Thought we were promising. Naïve would be a better description. We believed the bullshit we were fed about our brilliant futures.'

'That's a bit harsh.'

'It's a fact. I kept on believing and working my arse off and striving – remember our parents' faith in the virtue of striving? – for the top jobs that went to unprincipled shits like Baz Fuller. Or else the company folded. I must be a bad judge of failure potential.'

Alex said, 'In our cosy academic cocoon, we weren't trained to assess realities.'

'At least you're employed. I've resigned twice, been retrenched twice and barely escaped a prison sentence because I didn't spot the devious bastard who was conning me.' At that moment Doug was a poignant shadow of the cheerful man who had gone off to sell Jimbo Lamb's rotgut rum.

'I am employed, yes.' Alex, the consummate diplomat, was skilled at redirecting conversations. 'And I realise that life is much more exacting in the corporate fast lane than in government, where everything is ordained: gradual promotions, salary levels, the precise grade of office carpet and size of desk. At the end of it, if you're lucky, there'll be an honour – for which I won't qualify. Not quite out of the top drawer, you know? Scholarship man, regional accent, admitted poofter. The last handicap won't matter when more of us come out of the closet, but I'll never get the accent right, bah goom.'

Doug laughed and the evening was spared further post-mortems.

Alex phoned a week later to say that Rigby Vale needed a general manager, and was Doug interested?

'You're joking,' I heard him say on the phone in the hall.

There was a long conversation and he came through to my study looking stunned.

'Alex says that his golf estate in the Cape is looking for a general manager and I fit the bill: university background, corporate experience, physically fit, good with people and preferably South African. He's on the committee and says he can arrange an interview.'

My first reaction was, 'In the *Cape*? We'd be going home, and we've always said—'

'At least we should consider it. I've come to a dead end here.'

'What about my work?'

The acrid look he gave me said, Always thinking of yourself.

I swallowed panic and tried another tack. 'And the kids' schooling? They'll hate being uprooted to a foreign country.'

'Not so foreign. They've been there to see their grandparents.'

He was serious. 'Is this the kind of job you want, Doug?'

'Does it matter? Beggars can't be choosers.'

Trying to be constructive, I said, 'Would you like to manage a golf estate? You don't even play it.'

'Why not? They're not necessarily looking for a golfer. Initially I'd be coordinating construction – liaising between the companies building the houses, supervising the laying out of the course, landscaping and so on. When the project's complete, I'd be in charge of the business side of things and the assistant manager, who will handle estate maintenance, the groundsmen and the golfing facilities. Office hours only, Alex said. The major perk is a manager's house overlooking the central lake.'

'It was kind of him to think of you.'

'Shades of Jimbo's old boys' network, you mean?' His frown was so deeply grooved that it would never smooth out.

'Not Alex. He wouldn't recommend the job if he didn't

think it was right for you.' I bit back the swarming doubts and said, 'Fly there for an interview. We'll worry about decisions when you've seen what's on offer.'

What else could I say? His need was greater than ours.

*Dear Annie*
*My husband has just left me for another man. He says that he loves him and can't go on living a lie. But he promised he loved me before we got married. Now he says that he'll support me after the divorce and I should try and find my own happiness. The thing is, I still love him. It's so humiliating, I want to die. It's a good thing we don't have any children, or I would take them with me.*
*Desirée (that's a joke)*

*Dear Desirée*
*My heart aches for you. This is a very tough situation and you should see a professional counsellor to help you to come to terms with it. Please send your contact details so I can recommend someone who will help you.*
*Annie*

A wise granny or aunt could have helped her, but how many of us have access to older relatives with objective life experience we can depend on? The accepted wisdom then came prepackaged in magazines and how-to books like mine, not from the loving older women who once took such a keen interest in our lives.

## 27

He was offered the job and while we were debating the pros and cons, I lost mine.

*Modern Lifestyle* was about to mutate from its women's-only formula to focus on working professionals earning big salaries who couldn't be bothered with making do when they could afford to buy things. Lally planned to rename it simply *Modern* and revamp it in a punchy new format: neon-bright headlines, contemporary typefaces, highlighted quotes, slick photography. She said that readers no longer wanted style on a budget; they wanted instant chic and hip designer goods, and to hell with the expense.

'Get with it, Annie, if you want me to keep you on,' she warned. 'Besides being easy to prepare, I want food that's out of the ordinary and health-conscious. Give me the calorie count, fat and protein breakdown, trace elements, whatever you can dig up about scientific nutrition. I don't want cosy and twee any more.'

'I've never done cosy and twee!'

'Sure you have. It's the epitome of Annie Butterfield: meals around the fireplace, please your hubby with a birthday supper, etcetera. All that sixties shit is behind the moon. I want sleek. I want new. I want unisex and sophisticated. If you can't do it, I'll find someone better qualified. Plenty of cooking schools churning 'em out. Those puckish boys and girls buttoned up to the neck in starchy white are the culinary future. Photogenic as hell.

'So is their nouvelle cuisine: minimal servings, swirls of jus or raspberry coulis, dabs of balsamic reduction, courgette flowers, etcetera. Never mind that it won't feed a butterfly. Looks amazing.'

'But can those new chefs write?' I was aghast.

'Don't need to. My subs can tweak the copy.'

I could hardly breathe. She wanted to get rid of me. I stammered, 'But you've always said—'

'Never mind what I've always said. It's what readers want now. Headlines have got to scream the latest trends from the magazine racks.'

'You mean fads.'

'Whatever. And while we're on the subject, the same goes for *Annie Butterfield Advises.* Agony aunts are out, therapists are in. You've got to move with the times. The *Modern* reader sleeps around and gets STDs like genital warts and chlamydia. Faithful relationships are extinct. Rejection anxiety and panic attacks are big.'

I said feebly, 'I'll try, okay?'

'Get your mind around the new order fast, darling, or it's tickets.'

As usual she slammed the receiver down. The crunch had come. I was facing professional competition, even if it couldn't tell a sirloin from a silverside, or post-traumatic syndrome from the heebie-jeebies. I phoned Susie in a panic, but though she sympathised, she couldn't help. Her life was wall-to-wall with two small kids, increasing freelance work and helping with Xavier's practice.

During the next fortnight, I tried. I really tried. Two *Annie Butterfield Advises* and two sample cookery features later, gorgeously photographed by Zeke, Lally phoned with the verdict. 'They're not what I want for *Modern*.'

'They're not?' I could hardly breathe.

'No offence, but you're the wrong generation to dish up the required goods. We both need to move on. You can do a farewell party for the last *Modern Lifestyle* and that's that. I'm sure you understand.'

I couldn't detect even a tinge of remorse in her voice. I said, 'Out on my ear, then?'

'You can't say I didn't warn you. Repeatedly.'

'You did. And I've had a good run for my money. Your money.'

I must have tapped a residual milligram of regret, because she admitted, 'The new columnists have asked for double what you're getting. But I've beaten them down because they want the kudos. I learnt a lot from you, Anne. No journalist will ever hold me over a barrel again. I'll have others lined up in case anyone tries to blackmail me. Good ones are two a penny in the provinces now.'

'At least I've achieved something.' Now it was me sounding bitter.

'You've done a great job for longer than anyone could expect, and you know it. We'll run to five hundred quid for a farewell party, okay?'

'Gee, thanks.'

'Don't mensh.' And the phone clattered down leaving me to dissolve into tears of rage and loss.

The golf club's written offer to Doug arrived on the day I began planning the farewell party.

Because we were agonising over what to do, I didn't tell Mum and Dad, who had arrived in England on their annual visit. Mum had at last achieved her ambition: being on show at the Royal Academy. Granted, it was a special exhibition of work from various social centres, including the one in Richmond where she'd gone for painting lessons, but her finely detailed still life of trout on a marble slab next to a box of trout flies had been highly commended.

Standing beside Mum at the opening, I said, 'You're really good, you know? Those fish look as though they've just stopped twitching.'

'Thank you, dear. Despite the undertone of surprise.' She added, 'Dead trout don't move. A nice change from those restless well-hung young men.'

I had to laugh. 'Touché. And I'm not surprised. I love the painting you gave me. I'm so proud of you.' And I was. At sixty-seven my mother's cropped grey hair gave off a whiff of oil paints where her friends' reeked of beauty salon lacquer.

She put her arm through mine. 'That's a real accolade, coming from my famous daughter.'

'I won't be soon.'

'What do you mean?'

'Lally has fired me. "All that sixties shit" I've laboured over is out for the new magazine format, to be precise.'

'Nonsense. Don't listen to her.'

'It's done and dusted, Mum.'

'She's wrong. I know lots of people who buy it only for your articles.'

'They're probably of a certain age. Thoroughly un-*Modern*. Lally says that her new reader profile is twenty-five to thirty-nine, middle to high income, mostly professional or corporate. Not at all the women I've been writing for.'

'Look at me.' Mum swivelled me round to face her. 'I don't often give you advice, but I'm going to now. Brace yourself.'

I took a glass of wine from a passing tray. 'Braced.'

'Don't stop, Annie. You enjoy the work.'

'It's no good if the editor doesn't want what I do.'

'Give her what she wants, then. Visit the cooking schools and see what they're doing. Talk to counsellors about what's bothering young people today. I think you'll find they're the same old problems with different names.'

'It's too late. I'm past my sell-by date and writing regular features is damn hard work. It's time I did something else. Took on other projects.' I was trying to convince myself as much as her.

'What kind of projects?' Mum's over-the-specs look sharpened.

'I've been kicking around some ideas.'

I hadn't told her about the motivational books, partly

because I was afraid she'd find them trite, but there was a more pressing reason. I didn't want her and Dad to know the full extent of Doug's failure. They would have worried and his pride would have been even more dented if he'd got an inkling that the books had sustained us.

'You're being deliberately vague. Tell me.' Her antennae were fully extended by now.

I wriggled out of a confession by saying, 'I can't until things gel, and I'm truly tired of writing the columns. I need to pull out.'

She gave my arm an impatient shake. 'And lose your place as the self-help guru for families who can't afford experts? It's a shame.'

'That's just the point, don't you see? Lally's dropping the emphasis on family and doesn't want an amateur like me any more. Her new target market is far too sophisticated.'

'She's a fool and you're not an amateur. She'll change her tune when other editors start to make you offers.'

'I don't want to go on. It's been a long haul and I need a break.'

There were people buzzing all round us: preening artists and families awed by the famous surroundings, flashes going off, TV cameras prowling.

'You'll miss all this,' Mum warned. 'And it wouldn't be a break. It'd be permanent.'

'Too bad. It's time to do something completely different.'

'Just look before you leap, darling.'

Alex came up then to introduce himself and say that he'd bought her trout painting. It was Mum's first sale. As we left the Royal Academy in front of the men, she said, 'I'm walking on clouds. Who said old dogs can't learn new tricks?'

I couldn't help asking, 'And how goes the rumpty-tumpty?'

'Pretty amazing too.' And in the immortal words of Monty Python, she smiled quietly to herself.

Watching her, I was sorry that Budgie had stayed home with her sprogs who'd declined the honour of getting dressed up to be at Granny's opening. They'd have seen an older woman enjoying an evening of unexpected glory.

Lally was right about redesigning *Modern*. With the approach of the nineties, motherhood wasn't enough any more. Women no longer resigned themselves to years of child-rearing; they wanted more, and they wanted it *now*. Those who aimed to combine children with careers were also reading so many books about child-rearing that they were fearful of doing the wrong thing.

This is how Annie Butterfield signed off from answering queries in the final *Modern Lifestyle*.

*Dear Annie*
*What is it with kids today? You give them everything but they ask for more. You buy them toys, they want bikes. You give them five bob for the cinema on Saturday, they say no it's ten bob including popcorn and Coke. You go to the ends of the earth for holidays, and they want the moon. You tell them No, they scream Yes! My husband says why did we have them in the first place? I wonder why too. Surely there's more to life?*
*Roberta*

*PS Excuse me if I sound fed up with my kids, but they never think of me.*
*PPS Another thing: I don't know anyone I trust enough to leave them with.*

*Dear Roberta*
*You're right that there's more to life. You need regular breaks from kids, and also to let go of the idea that you're the only one who can be trusted. Look for a good babysitter so you can do things just for you: join a club, have coffee with friends, walk in the evenings with your husband and don't mention the kids once. I guarantee a change when they realise that you're not always available. Or a pushover.*
*Annie*

** This is the last letter from Annie Butterfield, dear readers, to be followed next month by a final column. It's been a privilege answering your queries all these years, and I thank you for letting me into your lives and hearts.*

## 28

Doug was alight with new hope but he was the only one. The rest of us were aghast at the idea of going to live in South Africa.

It took us a week to work through the discussions, arguments, moaning, weeping, dramatic denials, and sheer terror at the idea of leaving our lovely home, let alone England, for a country devastated by apartheid violence. TV newscasts towards the end of the eighties teemed with shots of evil-looking armoured vehicles crawling through clouds of teargas, bombed buildings, injured people and fist-waving funerals.

Robin demanded, 'How can you even *think* of making us all go to that terrible place?'

'It's where your mother and I come from,' was Doug's stock reply.

'It's not where *we* come from. And you're English citizens now.'

'We have dual nationality.'

'We don't.'

'You do actually, as our children. We registered you when

you were born. You have South African birth certificates that say "Pretoria Overseas".'

'We don't want to belong to that terrible place!' Tasha yelled.

'We'll get killed,' Chloe whispered.

'No, you won't. Alex says most of the trouble is confined to the townships, and he's been assured by experts that behind-the-scenes negotiations will stabilise the political situation. It's time for us to go home.'

'But it's not *our* home!' Tasha insisted.

Robin said, 'You're always telling us that so-called experts are bullshitting.'

'Not in this case. They're experienced diplomats. And we'd be leading a good life.' Doug was at his most persuasive, conjuring it up. 'There's a big house and a swimming pool. Sunshine and space. Rigby Vale means country living in the Winelands, close to an excellent co-ed school.'

'Co-ed – yuck!' Tasha shouted.

'I'm *at* an excellent school.' Robin's mouth was quivering.

'We don't want country living. We want to stay here,' Chloe wept.

'But I need to go.' Doug's face was a study in granite.

'You're crazy, Dad,' Robin said, then seeing his stricken look quickly added, 'I mean, this idea is nuts. We're happy here.'

'I'm not.'

Those were the two words that did it: resisting the move wasn't an option if the job restored him to the husband and father we loved. We'd uproot ourselves and trek halfway round the earth for Doug.

Except for Budgie. She said she was sorry, but she couldn't

change now. Each one of us tried to persuade her that she was part of the family and had to come too. Doug was the most persistent.

'You've been our pivot, Budge. Life wouldn't be the same without you.'

'We won't have hot scones waiting after school,' Chloe moaned.

'Who'll play cricket with us?' Robin demanded.

'You sprogs need to get on with your lives. Time to strike out on my own. Got some ideas.' Budgie used a brusque forefinger to dash away the first tears we'd ever seen her shed.

'Nooooooooo!' Tasha yelled, grabbing her in a hug.

But she was adamant. Budgie was our biggest loss.

There was more opposition from Dad when I told my parents, emphasising that we were going for Doug's sake. 'It's a great opportunity, a job he's really suited for. We all need the old Doug back.'

Dad said, 'I hope you know what you're doing, returning at this time. Things are looking bad now, whatever the diplomats are saying. A lawyer fellow called Albie Sachs just had his arm blown off by a car bomb in Mozambique.'

'That's outside the country, a long way from the Cape.'

'There's rioting in the townships too. And the news is censored.'

Mum's reaction was, after some thought, 'If you think it's the right thing to do, you must go. Even though I'll miss our visits. I'm just getting the hang of painting English clouds.'

'You could still come. I'd hate to cramp your style.' The teenage habit of revving up mothers dies hard.

'There'd hardly be any point if you've all gone. I can paint anywhere.' She went on with a speculating look over her glasses, 'The Cape has lovely mountains, come to think of it. We could move down there too.'

Decisions made, I worked on my farewell column as an agony aunt. The choice narrowed down to two interlinked topics: how to decide on your priorities in life and the importance of remaining true to yourself. I wanted to combine them into an extra-length feature but Lally said, 'No damn fear. I'm not paying any more than usual.' Typical. I'd be lucky to get a farewell cup of tea out of her.

It felt strange giving up the columns that had been my lifeline for so long, but it was also a relief to be done with deadlines and counselling people about their problems. The dire ones made me feel desperate for them and the squalid ones made me feel contaminated. Pleas from girls at the mercy of incestuous fathers and brothers were increasing in shocking numbers.

Quince said at our last meeting, 'You've done a wonderful job over the years, encouraging people to air their fears and worries.'

'With your help.'

'We've been a good team. I'll miss our debates over piles of letters, trying to decide which were the most needy or appealing.'

'We can still phone each other. And I'd love you to come out and stay with us.'

'One day, perhaps. It would be hard for me now,' she said.

'Kevin's been having spells of the DTs and there's serious liver damage – advanced cirrhosis. I'm going to take time off to nurse him. I don't know how long he'll last.'

'Oh, Quince.' I got up and put my arms round her and we hugged as people do when they say goodbye knowing it could be forever. We'd shared so much pain, both our own and others'.

Losing good friends like her and Budgie, who'd been staunch supports through hard times, was the worst thing about moving so far away.

To counteract the loss of income from the magazine, I'd written to my handbook publisher suggesting a series about careers and he'd said it was a great idea, stipulating that they should be open to women as well as men. 'The last thing we want is to appear sexist,' the letter of confirmation stressed.

It was a shrewd decision. Women's expectations of equality were soaring towards the end of the twentieth century. Most of us would be flabbergasted by the subsequent growth of fundamentalism that confined women to their traditional roles – as much in the American Bible Belt and the Vatican hierarchy as in the Middle East and Africa.

Like so many of my generation, I am far more of a feminist than my daughters, who don't perceive sex discrimination as a problem. Despite the trauma of emigrating, Tasha and Chloe would bubble along in their busy lives, assured that they could choose any career they liked, oblivious of most women's struggles for equal pay and access to the corridors of power. And still ignorant, as I had been until well after I married, of men's complexities.

Alex, their much loved honorary uncle, had complexities which they were just beginning to realise.

'He's gay, isn't he?' Tasha demanded after he had taken them to a posh restaurant and a Saturday matinee of the Royal Ballet in Covent Garden as a leaving-England gift.

'Yes.' I wouldn't even have thought of the question at their age. We didn't use the word 'gay' either.

'But he doesn't have a partner,' Chloe objected. 'It must be lonely.'

'Specially without kids. That's why he likes us so much,' Tasha said.

'We should try and find him someone nice. What about—?'

And Chloe named a show-jumper at their riding school while I marvelled at our different mindsets. They may have taken the achievements of feminists for granted, but they were far more open than my generation about the sexual freedoms that had been won.

I had teenagers like them in mind when I wrote my final column.

***Annie Butterfield Advises***

*These are my last words as your sympathetic problem solver, and I'm addressing them to young readers who will be leaving school in the not-too-distant future.*

*Shakespeare gave one of his most famous lines to Polonius, who told his son Laertes in* Hamlet*: 'This above all: to thine own self be true.'*

*If you're true to yourself and secure in your tried and tested beliefs, the Force is with you. But don't expect equality.*

***Annie advises:*** *Of course we're not equal! We're as different from each other as any one species can be. Your task is to discover your uniqueness and learn to treasure it, to the point where you can honestly say, 'I like the person I am.' That's being true to yourself…*

Etcetera, etcetera. I could churn out the stuff in my sleep now, though all along I'd stuck to a simple principle: write from the heart. Lally's longstanding *Modern Lifestyle* readers were outraged when she dropped both my features with the excuse that the new *Modern* format needed fresh new voices. But she struggled to replace me with journalists who could spell and write common sense. Lally was a perfectionist who expected the best and flew into a rage with anything less. My replacement 'personal counsellor' wrote pop-psycho gobbledygook.

I felt vindicated when *Modern*'s circulation dropped more than thirty per cent after I was fired. Lally's secretary sent on a fat packet of letters from readers who had written in, the most memorable of which read:

*Dear Editor*
*A pox on the new format. May you be doomed forever to consort with hideously maimed mountain goats bleating dirges. You've left us in the bleeding lurch, letting Annie go. Her down-to-earth, pithy counsel has been glorious music to ears accustomed to the puerile bleating of media sheep. I am cancelling my subscription forthwith.*
*Dorothy*

*Dear Annie*
*You told me to believe in myself and trust my instincts, which you said were what I really know deep down inside. I just want to thank you because what I really know is I'm not stupid. I got my O levels last year and now I'm trying for my A levels. Cool, or what?*
*Our Dawn*

None of the letters had addresses so I couldn't answer or thank the writers, but I kept the best ones in a file to remind myself on blue days that Annie Butterfield had made a difference to a lot of lives.

# 29

The grand finale from Annie Butterfield's kitchen was planned for the week before we left: a spectacular buffet with an array of trendy dishes that I hoped would pull the rug out from under the next incumbent's feet. Xavier negotiated an elegant dining room in the Royal Institute of British Architects for the venue. Some of his clients and their wives, who were happy to be photographed, were invited to enjoy the feast.

Zeke wasn't surprised at the turnout. He said, 'People love being in the public eye,' as he set up his tripod to photograph the feast before guests were allowed in.

'Can't think why.'

'But you've enjoyed it, haven't you?'

He squinted up at me over his favourite camera, an old Mamiya Press with a wide-angle lens that used 120 colour film for richly detailed 6 × 9 transparencies. He was over seventy then, his hair and eyebrows wirier than ever, though faded from iron filings to hoar frost. I'd miss Zeke's congenial presence in my kitchen, setting up lights and cameras and reflective umbrellas as Budgie and Susie and I laid out the food and flowers and place settings to his specifications. His sense of style came from the Old Masters: he could turn a meal into a Vermeer interior or make a picnic look like a scene painted by Monet or Pissarro, all foaming trees and dappled sunlight.

'Up to a point,' I said. 'It was nice being taken seriously and treated as an authority, but I'd rather have stayed anonymous.'

'Wouldn't have worked. Readers like genuine. It's important that they know there's a real Anne behind Annie Butterfield.'

'Lally thinks the real Anne's cooking is too twee and cosy for today's *Modern* readers. I don't exude the nouvelle cuisine ethos.'

'Makes no sense.' Zeke was fiddling with a lens. 'She's taking a gamble, changing her format. The circulation will drop. But yes, it's time for you to quit.'

'You mean I'm getting stale?'

'Not at all. No need to be offended.' He lifted his head and I saw that the kind brown eyes were ringed with faded blue. 'I think you've run your course in the kitchen. Leave all the fussing with food to the eager beaver youngsters, eh? You have wisdom to impart. Life experience.'

He was saying what I'd felt. 'Not any more. Lally wants a lifestyle coach and is also dropping *Annie Butterfield Advises.*'

'Ah now, that's a big pity. Many readers will miss you.'

'Thanks. And I'll miss you.' I had a lump in my throat.

'Will I see you again, Zeke?' Budgie was buffing up the silver cutlery for the shoot, standing very straight in the too-big navy trouser suit she had bought for the photographs of the two of us on this final occasion.

He lumbered over to put his arm round her shoulders.

'Course I'll come to the house before you all leave, Budge. Your cream scones are the best of the best. I'll miss them like hell.'

She tilted her head to look up at him, and for just a moment I caught a brightness under her eyelids. 'You'd better come, buster, or you're dead meat.'

He chuckled and gave her a mighty squeeze before going back to his camera while I stood with comprehension dawning. I'm not sure whether Zeke realised she was in love with him, but I do know that he still mourned his cruelly lost wife and baby daughter. He'd told me once, to explain why Ginger had broken up with him, 'All my life I will wake and go to sleep with my darlings.'

It was a moment of revelation. All of us had come to rely on good old Budgie as a spunky friend and helper without acknowledging that she was a woman too. And I thought, It's definitely time Annie Butterfield retired if she can't see what's happening under her nose. I'm sure it was the loss of Zeke that inspired Budgie to pour her affection into the spy novels by 'Victor B Smail' that she began to write after we left. I sometimes wonder if I should have tried to bring them together – *Matchmaking Annie Advises.*

And then I tell myself that we're governed by fate and if it was to be, it would have happened without my interference.

The final buffet was a masterpiece and Zeke did it proud in photographs lit like a Rembrandt. Since Lally was paying for the last time, it was served with French wines and flutes of Moët & Chandon.

The starters at one end were a whole side of smoked salmon

garnished with thin lemon slices; a platter of blini with a bowl of caviar on crushed ice and small dishes of sour cream, finely chopped onion and hard-boiled egg; and melon wrapped in Parma ham.

The main dishes in the middle were rare roast beef fillet with salsa verde and deep fried capers; crumbed lamb cutlets with mint sauce; vitello tonnato with fettuccine; spanakopita (spinach and feta cheese in phyllo pastry); caprese and green salads.

For dessert at the other end there were: tiramisu (the latest thing then); pears poached in red wine; tarte tatin with crème frâiche; lemon syllabub in long-stemmed glasses; petits fours; and a board of English cheeses.

Xavier's clients raved – and so did Lally's readers, many of whom wrote and telephoned, threatening to stop buying the magazine if she dropped Annie Butterfield.

But it was too late for either of us to change our minds. Annie's column was dated and so was its logo, the old-fashioned blue and white Cornishware jug.

The housing market was in the doldrums so we didn't sell the house for much more than we'd paid, but the burden of the mortgage was gone. Robin and Tasha and Chloe partied with their friends, vowing that they'd never lose touch and would be back as soon as their brutal parents released them from the clutches of a new continent and a strange colonial high school where girls had classes with boys.

Budgie bought a flat in Chiswick and a typewriter. We all speculated over why she needed it, though she brushed off our questions with, 'To pester you all with letters. I'll expect screeds back about the luxury living out there.'

'Come with us, *please*,' the kids begged, but she was adamant.

'You sprogs will be out of the house soon. Won't need an effing old has-been like me. Besides –' she put in quickly '– I've got other fish to fry.'

We tried to wheedle out her intentions, but true to her name she wouldn't budge. 'State secret. You'll know if things pan out.'

She was everywhere when the packers came with their boxes and cartons and rolls of wrapping paper and plastic, bossing them about and supervising the stowing of our worldly goods into the back of a giant removal van. The furniture and large appliances went first, covered by blankets, with the packing cases and dozens of smaller cartons filling in the gaps, including those that held our books and my copies of the motivational bestsellers.

I stood looking out the window of the study where I'd worked for so long, thinking, There goes our life, all trussed up into cubic feet. How did we accumulate all that stuff? We had so little when we came to England: just a few wedding presents and the canteen of stainless steel cutlery that we still use, though only in the kitchen now.

With every fibre of my apprehensive being, I hoped we were doing the right thing.

# 30

The voyage south on a cruise ship sailing from Southampton was a limbo time for all of us. The children alternated between moping in their cabins, shrieking over deck games and wallowing in the swimming pool on the upper deck, where the water heaved from side to side and fruit drinks were served in frosted glasses with little umbrellas.

Doug exercised ruthlessly in the ship's gym, saying he was getting fit for the fray. Often he stood in the prow gazing ahead as if trying to imagine life beyond the horizon. I lay on a deckchair reading, limp as a convalescent after a serious illness. We all missed Budgie buzzing around.

'It's like we've lost Mary Poppins,' Chloe lamented.

'Only she swears like a fucking dustman,' Tasha said.

'We'll have to clean up our act in the new school.' Robin was facing the social death of a senior year with no friends.

When the ship steamed towards Cape Town harbour early one morning with that implausible blue mountain rearing up, we stood in an anxious line along the rail watching the approach of an unknown future.

Mum and Dad were at the quayside to meet us, having moved into an Edwardian double-storey in Gardens big enough to accommodate us all while Doug started his job. The manager's house was still being built: spacious, bland and not a patch on our lovely home by the river, but it overlooked a lake where he could row with a view of vineyards and mountains.

I won't go into the problems of living with older parents for three months and settling teenagers into a school where they didn't know anyone and everything was different, not least the upside-down seasons. They had to come to terms with a hot windy Christmas, sunburn, a vibrant maelstrom of unfamiliar languages, and bewildering customs. No doubt they'll tell their own stories blaming us for the fault line in their lives. But this is Doug's and my story.

He thrived on the challenge of setting up and running the Rigby Vale golf estate. At last he had found a job where his personality and experience were valued. His own struggles with failure and frustration made him a sympathetic mediator in the inevitable disputes between architects, builders, landscapers and, later, club members and estate residents.

During the construction phase he worked six days a week, roaring off at sunrise in a Land Rover with a yellow hard hat on the back seat. His prefab office was lined with plans and flowcharts above a haphazard line-up of desks, drawing boards and a table-sized model of the project. When I was roped in to man the phone for a week while the site secretary was on leave, men trooped in and out all day with requests and complaints. It was a madhouse that would have driven me nuts, but Doug revelled in doing what he called, 'A useful job at last. They need me, Annie. I'm bloody good at this.'

His ebullience spilled like sunshine over us and pumped him up with confidence. He spent as much time out of doors as dealing with problems in the office. Prowling the building sites and overseeing the layout of the golf course, service roads, the artificial lake and extensive landscaping made him lean and fit and gave him a deep tan. He began to take golf lessons as the course developed, and on Saturdays spent time with Alex – who'd emigrated a month after us – in the greenhouses.

Alex had begun to collect orchids as an antidote to Whitehall, he said, but I think it was his practical way of filling the void left by Geoffrey. He often said that we were his family now. Robin and the twins adored their honorary uncle, though there were times when he wore a look of acute loss.

To my surprise, I was the one who found the transition most difficult. After a life that had revolved round my family and constant work, it was a comedown to be confined to school lifts and choosing finishes for the new house. I had abandoned my trusty typewriter to buy a newfangled little computer with a printer before we left England, thinking I could practise how to use the things before getting stuck into a new handbook. But they squatted greyly on the desk Mum had installed in our bedroom, defying my attempts to understand their enigmatic workings.

'Take a course at the Tech,' she suggested. 'You need to learn something called Windows.'

'I'm too old and experienced for Tech,' I snapped. 'There are manuals, for pete's sake.'

'Suit yourself,' she said before breezing off to the nearby

Michaelis School of Fine Art, where she had already signed up for a degree course, having organised an extra helper to do all the housework an expanded family entailed.

Because my pride wouldn't allow me to knuckle down and join a class of Matric-leavers, I had to struggle through those bloody manuals on my own, and the long process eclipsed any idea of writing. I was back to square one – a dependent daughter – and a fate I'd never had to face: being a mother in a strange city with nothing to do but wrestle with new technology and worry about kids who needed her less and less.

And Doug didn't need me either. His position as general manager of an upmarket golf estate meant that he was invited to sporting events and tournaments, and to sit on sports administration committees. When the construction phase was over, there was a second metamorphosis: the Land Rover gave way to a Volvo and his work clothes to urbane blazers with open-neck shirts. With his hair glinting silver and the civil Oxford manner that gets more pronounced with the years, he was a quality product like a veteran Rolls or Bentley.

I felt like the old Vauxhall we'd given to Budgie when we left: second-hand, out of date and needing a new battery and spark plugs.

For four of the five months it took the builders to complete our new house, I yearned for my typewriter and nearly bought a new one. Then Robin took pity on me and passed on enough of his computer lessons at the new school to get me to the point where I could create a document and save it onto a floppy. While his impatience at my slowness to learn the new discipline was humbling, it clearly gave him a kick to be teaching his know-it-all mother, until cricket started consuming most of his spare time.

Being good at sport helped him to be absorbed into teams, and soon the girls were busy teenagers too, clamouring to go with new friends to the movies or the beach. When we moved into the house that smelt of fresh paint and new carpets, the school was close enough for them to walk there and back, and life soon settled down to a routine. I plugged on with the first planned handbook and did necessary lifting in the second-hand Mercedes station wagon we'd bought as a family car. Doug rowed in the evenings and ate his midday meals in the clubhouse, often coming in quite late. The teenagers became sandwich-grabbers between activities. Since the workload was light, our weekday cleaning lady Philisa left at one for an afternoon job. Sometimes it was only me sitting down to a salad.

For the first time in my life, I knew what it was to be lonely. Even bored sometimes, the queen bee with no acolytes – not even a drone. Doug was so chuffed with being the breadwinner who had provided his family with a new life in a magnificent hive that I couldn't spoil it with complaints or regrets.

When she realised that I was foundering, Mum said, 'Didn't you say that you had books to write?'

'I'm working on one, but missing Budgie and my friends. Even Lally's ranting sometimes. It's so quiet out here.'

'You've forgotten how bad things were. Look on the bright side.'

Though the clichés were irritating, she was right: I'd forgotten. I wrote to my publisher, who phoned to say that he'd advertised the new series of career handbooks and was waiting for the first manuscript. So I put my head down and thrashed the computer keyboard into submission, pleased to be wanted again.

Soon enough Robin was the god-like captain of the school eleven, resplendent in cricket whites as he chatted up girls. The twins flourished like jungle vines at their various pursuits, growing by inches as they responded to the potent fertiliser of a stimulating school and a once more happy home.

Our family enterprise was back on an even keel again. Those were the years when we lived the dream.

# 31

The year 1989 was an increasingly fraught year of riots, limpet mines and killings, offset by Archbishop Tutu's peace march through the Cape Town streets. Robin learnt that he'd passed Matric a few weeks before Mandela walked free on 11 February 1990 after twenty-seven years in prison. With three friends, Robin made his way to the city's Grand Parade to join the masses listening to the great man speak before they left to backpack in Europe.

I thought he was far too young to travel. He could make breakfast, keep his room tidy and use a vacuum cleaner, but had never had to fend for himself. I produced a number of good reasons why he shouldn't go but Doug said, 'Stop mother-henning him. He needs to stand on his own two feet for a change.'

Fathers have been saying that for centuries. I countered with, 'He's still so young and backpacking is dangerous. What if he gets into trouble?'

'He'll be with friends. And he *has* friends in England.'

'They're all boys!'

'Young men of nineteen, you mean. At their age I was working on the railways during the summer to earn my pocket money for the rest of the year. My family wasn't well off like yours.'

'That's not the issue here, Doug. I just don't think we should let him go wandering around god knows where. He should be studying.'

'He needs to grow up a bit first, know what it's like to be hard up and hungry. I say we give him an air ticket and a basic allowance for a year. If he needs more, he can work for it like I did.'

I gave in on conditions. He had to promise to use buses and trains, not to hitch-hike or get into vehicles with strangers, to write to us once a week and phone home reverse charges once a month. Or if in trouble.

Robin was ecstatic. 'Thanks, guys! It's going to be amazing.'

He and his friends joined the Youth Hostel Association, bought backpacks, sleeping bags and hiking boots, and set off for London with four tearful mothers watching their plane take off from the airport balcony. They'd have been mortified if their cheering friends in International Departures had spotted us.

Tasha and Chloe were furious. 'You'd never let us go.'

'Of course not. You haven't finished school yet.'

'Because we're *girls.*' From Tasha.

'That's true.' I couldn't help smiling.

'Don't laugh! Boys have all the fun. They're allowed to go to places on their own.'

'Robin's always been your favourite,' Chloe accused me.

'Your blue-eyed boy,' Tasha said.

'That's *not* true.' I'd never had a favourite child.

'But you bought him Doc Martins when we weren't allowed them.'

'*And* he's got his own bedroom when we have to share.'

'*And* you let him go to pop concerts.'

They went on dragging up grievances – some from the distant past – until we agreed to compensate them with a special treat. Doug had the idea of flying up to Joburg for a long weekend and when I protested about the expense, gave me his old up-curving smile and said, 'We're flush now that I have a decent job. I want to spoil my three girls in the flesh-pots. Sandton City, here we come.'

And he did spoil us. It was heaven, with plays and movies and shopping and exhilarating love-making after the twins had nodded off to exhausted sleep in the next-door suite.

One afternoon in early December when the doorbell rang, I found a scruffy backpacker beaming through a beard and dreadlocks who said, 'Mum! It's me.'

His postcards had been sporadic despite the promises, though occasional requests for small amounts of extra cash had kept us informed that he was alive.

'Robin?' What I could see of his face was thin and weathered.

'The very same.' He flung his arms round me, smelling of sweat and smoke and musty clothes that hadn't known soap for a while.

'You didn't write very often,' I moaned in the general direction of his ear. 'Where have you been? How did you get back?'

'Overland, via Egypt and Ethiopia and Kenya. Buses, ferries, trains, long-distance trucks, you name it.'

'You look so different.'

'I *am* different. I've decided to be a farmer.' He pulled back with a triumphant smile.

'Oh no,' was all I could manage. Before leaving he'd been accepted at UCT to do science. Robin had always been more of a sportsman than a swot but his marks were more than adequate for university. We'd thought of him as a lazy learner who would blossom when he committed to a career. And how right we proved to be.

He said, 'Oh yes. I like working in the open air and I'm not going to be cooped up in an office being bossed around. Ever.'

'Dad won't like it. He's set on university for you.'

'Don't think you can put me off.' A fierce glare penetrated the thickets of fuzz. 'I've made my decision.'

Tasha came charging out of the kitchen. 'Bloody hell, Robin, you're back!'

Chloe followed her saying, 'About time too. And I heard what you're planning. You know Dad won't be keen.'

He enveloped them both, saying, 'It's my life. I don't want to make the same mistakes he did.'

I appealed to him over their heads. 'It was different for Dad. For all of us after the war. We didn't have the choices you have today.'

'He went to Oxford. He had plenty of choices there and afterwards, and he stuffed them all up.'

'Let me go,' Chloe demanded, and when she had wriggled loose said, 'You're wrong. He tried so hard.'

I added the familiar words I hadn't used since we'd left England. 'And he was unlucky.'

'Unlucky, hell.' Robin's jeer was so like Doug's when he was angry: the same derision, the same frowning glower. 'He was a square peg in a succession of round holes – I heard you say it, Mum. I'm going to do something fulfilling.'

I tried a warning. 'He'll be upset. He'll insist.'

'Too bad. It's not his life, it's mine. If he says he won't – or can't – pay for my training, I'll get a student loan.'

'You *mustn't* let him hear you say that,' I hissed. 'He can easily afford to pay now. Don't challenge him that way.'

'It's a son's duty to challenge his father. I'm going to Cedara in Natal. I applied from the South African Embassy in Athens and they accepted me.'

'So it's done.'

'And dusted. No use carrying on about it, Mother.'

I started fussing at the straps of his backpack saying, 'I remember Cedara as a place for rich farmers' sons whose daddies can afford to set them up on their own farms. Or thickos whose parents don't know where the hell else to send them.'

My once-amiable Robin swung on me blazing with contempt. 'That's patronising crap! I didn't know you were a snob.'

'Not a snob, and you know it.'

'All graduates are the same. So are people who've worked for big organisations,' he added quickly. 'You think an important job or a piece of paper from a university makes you better than anyone else. Well, it's not true. I've met some fantastic people on the road. Real people. Workers.'

Tasha took the backpack he was shrugging off. 'Signed up

for the great unwashed, our brother. Never mind, Mum, he'll come round.'

'I won't come round! And I haven't joined the great unwashed.'

'Could have fooled us.' Chloe grinned at him. 'I suggest you head for the shower before Dad gets home if you want to impress him with your revelations. He's not going to listen to a tramp.'

'Leave my stuff alone. I'm quite capable of dealing with it.' Robin snatched the backpack away from Tasha. 'And they're not revelations. You've all got to stop treating me like a kid.'

'But you are,' I said. Foolishly.

'Not any longer. I've experienced life. And I want to be a farmer because it's a real job. I've harvested sugar beet and worked in vineyards and on a pig farm where I mucked out the sties and delivered new litters. I've learnt to drive tractors and use rotavators. I'm really interested in organic farming. This is an informed decision, not a passing phase. You'd all better get used to it.'

Admitting that your little boy has turned into a man isn't easy, but I saw that his eyes gleamed with purpose. He was far more mature and – yes – experienced than I'd been as a green girl leaving school for university.

I said, 'I believe you, Robin. But it's all very sudden. We'll make decisions when Dad comes home, okay?'

'There's nothing to decide except who's going to pay.' He stomped off to the utility room to stuff his clothes into the washing machine.

Doug was tired when he came home, and his delight at seeing Robin soured as soon as he heard about his intention to go to Cedara.

'Absolutely not,' was his first reaction. 'You're going to university.'

'Absolutely *not*,' Robin flared. 'I've explained why. It's my life, Dad.'

'And you want to throw it away on farming?'

'I want to spend it usefully.'

Doug glared at him. 'Unlike me, you mean?'

'I didn't say that. It's just that I'm a practical guy and I want to work with my hands. Cricket was my best thing at school, remember? Not the academic stuff.' Robin was pleading now.

'You agreed to go to university. You applied. They accepted you. It's an honour, understand? You can't turn down a chance like that.' Doug was being pompous, an attitude that seemed to have grown on him since the new job.

'I've changed my mind about what I want to do.'

'You can't just change your mind. When you're accepted for something you applied for, you have to stick to it.' Doug slammed his glass of wine down, radiating scorn. 'I won't have a son of mine shilly-shallying over his future.'

There was a long silence as they glared at each other.

Then Robin said, 'Jesus, Dad, what has running this place done to you? That's what a self-important old fart would say.'

'How dare you!'

Robin got up, a vagabond with wild hair who bore no likeness to the dashing cricket captain who had left on his travel odyssey. 'I dare because it's important. Nothing you say will change my mind.'

'I won't pay.'

'You don't have to. I'll get a student loan.'

'Son—' For a moment Doug wavered and I could see shards of his old despair under the new assurance, then he recovered and said, 'It's your life, agreed. Do as you please with it. Just don't ask me to approve. Or finance you.'

'Oh, I won't. And fuck you too.' Robin was gone, leaving the rest of us to a silent meal.

I paid, of course, on the understanding that he didn't tell Doug. The handbooks were doing well and I had stashed the royalties in a separate savings account against a rainy day. Robin's decision bore out what I came to believe in my long years as an agony aunt: that people are born with their basic natures, and though parents can augment and enrich their children's lives, it's playing with fire to try to influence their deeply felt choices.

We didn't see much of him after he went to Cedara, as he spent his holidays working on farms. When he did come home during brief visits to friends in Cape Town, he chose times when Doug would be out. The three of us hung on his stories about the life he found so satisfying. Chloe, still besotted with animals, was beside herself with envy and said she wanted to go to Cedara too and work with livestock. Tasha begged him to teach her how to drive a tractor.

In that warm circle, chatting and laughing, we had some good times before the real rainy days came.

## 32

One of the requirements for senior staff at Rigby Vale was an annual check-up at a health and wellness clinic for executives. Doug enjoyed the full-day cosseting which included metered exercise on various machines, blood and lung capacity tests, x-rays and an ECG followed by a thorough medical examination, all of which produced an assessment of his state of health. He'd come home after the final full-body massage with a file of charts and comments measuring his performance against the base year, 1988, which were well above average for his age. Cycling as a youngster, cross-country running and squash at university, and regular rowing ever since had kept him in peak physical condition, always a source of pride.

'Quite a bod, eh?' he'd say in our early years together, admiring himself naked in front of the mirror.

'Great bod,' I'd reply, hugging it. I always loved the warm-apples scent of his skin. He never smelt of sweat after exercise and he'd come out of the shower in a glow of vigour, his dark hair as sleek as a seal's until it dried and sprang back into the familiar thick wedge.

The years of patchy employment had given him an ironic advantage: time to exercise beyond the level of his peers. Except during the months of his deepest depression, the physical pleasure of solitary rowing always made him feel better and more optimistic. He was far more active than most men of his age and super-fit. So it was a shock to both of us when one of the blood tests showed a slight rise in his PSA.

I felt a clutch of dread at the pinched whiteness round his mouth as he told me. 'What's that?'

'Prostate-specific antigen. It's gone up from four to five point two five. No enlargement found during the rectal exam, though.' He spoke like an automaton programmed with medical jargon.

'What does it mean?'

'I have to go back every three months for more tests.'

'Oh, Doug.'

We stood with our arms round each other for the longest time. Then he said, 'They reckon it may be just a temporary blip,' and went upstairs to change out of the new tracksuit he had bought for the occasion. The old one had got shabby during his supervisory jogs round the estate, 'Killing two birds with one stone,' he called it, 'keeping fit while I work.' Alex often jogged with him to discuss problems like diseased patches on the greens or what to do about the pigeon droppings at the clubhouse entrance.

The next three blood tests showed no change, then Doug began to have trouble peeing. It took him longer and he had to go more often, getting up several times in the night. By the fourth test – at the January 1993 full check-up – his PSA had risen to seven and his prostate was enlarged. I heard his car pull into the drive but he stayed in it until I went out and opened the door.

Without looking at me, he got out saying, 'It's up again. This is serious, Annie. I have to see a urologist for a needle biopsy.'

'Is it—?' I couldn't say the word. Not then.

Nor could he. 'Can't tell yet. The biopsy will show anything … untoward. Don't mention it to Robin, okay?' So he knew that I kept in touch.

He insisted on driving to the Claremont Clinic on his own, saying it was just a brief procedure and he didn't need me holding his hand. The biopsy was clear but the urologist told him that needle samples were hit or miss and recommended monthly blood tests, 'To keep an eye on things.'

Doug phoned to tell me the result, then went to work and told Alex, asking him not to say anything to the estate committee. 'It's none of their business – yet,' he said when he got home.

'What do you mean, "yet"?'

He gave me the look I remembered so well from the bad days: sarcastic with an edge of self-mockery. 'You don't get it, do you?'

'What don't I get?'

'The whole point of executive clinics is to suss out problems in senior men before they begin to affect performance. The check-ups are expensive, but give employers time to find replacements before their investments are compromised by failing health or mental instability. It's a sneak assessment. Totally cynical.'

'I thought it was a perk that came with the job.'

'Perk, hell. Self-interest rules in commerce. Of all people, you should know that. Lally is a perfect example of the breed.'

'Golf estates are hardly commerce.'

'They're worse! Investments in an upmarket development like Rigby Vale are dependent on people's perception of its value. If the management shows signs of faltering, residents complain like hell and threaten to leave. If it slips any further, they sell up and go – quickly, before it gets an iffy reputation. Then they bad-mouth the place and soon nobody wants to buy in. It's a lifestyle we've sold them, not just real estate. Why do you think I've been so good at the job?'

'Because you're well-qualified and work hard.' He was getting so angry that I was afraid he might explode if I didn't say the right thing.

'That's just for starters. It's also because I look and speak right. I fit in. I'm the commander of the fleet with gold braid on his sleeves and an impressive tan who keeps everything steaming along nicely. If I lose my touch or start to look seedy, the whole picture changes. A general manager who's going downhill could affect everyone's investments.'

'But you've done so well. The estate committee can hardly fire you for not feeling—'

'And you're so damn naïve, Annie! Don't you understand that I'll be out on my ear the moment they realise I've got something serious wrong with me? I'm back on the slippery slope. Just when I thought I was home and dry.' He flung away towards the kitchen chanting, 'Buzz, buzz, buzz, buzz, busy bee, busy bee, buzz if you like but don't sting me.'

'What's wrong, Dad?' I heard Tasha say.

'Everything. There's a question mark hanging over my health.'

'But – but you're so strong and fit,' Chloe said.

'Not any more.' His despairing cry reverberated through the house.

The twins were at different universities by then: Tasha studying biokinetics at Stellenbosch and Chloe having elected for zoology at UCT. To nobody's surprise, she plunged into rodent genetics as a volunteer on a research team. Doug christened her Ratgirl with the exaggerated affection of a father denied the chance to be proud of his son.

It took me a long time to understand why he remained so adamant that Robin had thrown his life away on farming, even after he'd achieved top marks in his final year at Cedara and been invited to do honours at the Natal University Agricultural Faculty.

'Robin's done so well,' I'd plead.

Only to be answered by, 'Any fool can be a farmer.'

'He's not a fool,' I'd insist, 'and he's at university now.'

'Narrowing your choice of career is foolish. I should know.'

The penny dropped. It was about Doug's own misjudgements, not Robin's choice of what his father considered a non-profession.

Words can't describe what Doug went through. His PSA kept rising and a second biopsy detected cancer cells. The urologist referred him to a specialist surgeon who gave him two options: 'Radiation or surgery. The good news is that cancer of the prostate is slow-growing and usually well contained, often for years. Since your previous biopsy was clear, it's probably at an early stage. The prognosis is good if the tumour hasn't metastasised and we catch it in time.'

'Which would you recommend?' Doug's voice was beyond bleak. I was sitting in the chair next to him, having been allowed to hold his hand at the final stage of this crucial consultation.

'I'll give it to you straight, Mr Perceval.' The surgeon's bluff compassion was a relief after the impersonal urologist who had refused to talk to Doug if I was present. 'Radiation's still a bit hit and miss. To be on the safe side in cases like yours, I recommend a radical prostatectomy with nerve-sparing, which means that you may be able to function again in time. No guarantees, though,' he added.

'Function?'

'Have marital relations. You'll be impotent after the operation. For a while, anyway.'

There was a long silence while Doug took this in, then he said, 'And if it has spread?'

'There are further options. We'll do a bilateral orchiectomy if necessary and there's hormone therapy. But I wouldn't be too concerned at this stage. It's early days. And we have aids for penile dysfunction, including injections and a vacuum pump that works pretty well. I'd suggest counselling too.'

'All I need,' Doug muttered.

'Believe me, it's not the end of the world.' The surgeon stood up and held out his hand. 'Go home and discuss it together, then give me a ring about your decision.'

Doug was silent on the drive home until I said, 'What's a bilateral orchiectomy?'

'It means cutting off both your balls. I'm fucked, Annie.'

'That's not what the surgeon said. It's early days still.'

I put my hand on his arm for comfort, but he shrugged it off and tightened his hands on the steering wheel until his knuckles turned white. 'Doesn't matter how early. I can see it all coming: first I lose my job, then my health, then my balls. We'll have to find a new place to live in and you'll have to put up with an unemployed eunuch hanging around. That's if I survive.'

'You'll be fine, darling. You're so fit and strong.'

'Cock-eyed optimist,' was his only reply, then and later when we had made the decision.

It was useless trying to get any other response as his anxiety deepened in the run-up to the operation at the end of January 1993. I wonder now if his inborn pessimism contributed to, or even attracted, the bad luck that dogged him like a persistent shadow?

One of the issues between us during the bad years had been his belief that I'd been unusually lucky in my life – which I had, of course – and perhaps drained off his share of luck. Once in the middle of a very dark night he'd accused me of being a succubus. In the morning he'd laughed it off and said it had been part of a nightmare, but the idea had burrowed like a parasitic worm into my mind. Now I woke often with the thought: What if the cancer is my fault? What if I've caused him more stress than his body could handle, leaving it vulnerable to this most opportunistic of dread diseases?

Living with the guilt was even harder than the ominous apprehension.

With the date of the operation set, Doug had to tell the estate committee. They gave him three months' sick leave, 'And more if you need it, my dear fellow,' the chairman said, radiating concern. 'We are all far too intimately acquainted with our urologists not to sympathise.'

'Crocodile tears, or what?' Doug asked Alex at supper that night. 'He's such a verbose old dinosaur.'

The twins were out at a party and the three of us were sharing a bottle of merlot.

Alex said, 'I haven't heard anything untoward. We all develop problem prostates in the end.'

'That's what he inferred. But I'm afraid they'll write me off.'

'You're jumping the gun. Let's see how everything goes, eh? It's usually a very successful operation. I've heard that Geoffrey had the same procedure a while back and he's still fine.'

Doug blurted, 'Is he impotent?'

'I wouldn't know.' Alex twiddled his wine glass. 'We've done the honourable thing and not contacted each other since he married.'

'Sorry. That was uncalled for.' Doug flushed and began to tremble, which had happened several times since we'd seen the surgeon.

Alex leant over and gripped his arm. 'Courage, mon ami. It's a bloody awful prospect. But not final, you know?'

'Thanks.' They exchanged a long look and the trembling stopped.

Alex's hand wasn't shaken off as mine had been. Men have a particular solidarity when it comes to their privates – as women do. I've sat with friends after hysterectomies who sobbed their eyes out at not being 'complete' any more, even after years of pain and heavy bleeding. Now Alex could console Doug far better than I could: his adoring succubus.

The operation lasted two and a half hours and he went into intensive care afterwards with a nerve block that made him numb from the waist down. When I was allowed in to see him, masked and gowned, I found him deathly pale and hooked up to several tubes, but lucid.

'Can't feel a thing,' were his first mumbled words, followed by, 'Is it over?'

'It's all over. You've done fine, sailed through. The surgeon says there was no involvement of the glands.' He'd said 'no apparent involvement', to be precise, but asked me not to pass that on.

'Thank God. Now you can tell Robin.' Doug's heavy eyelids fell as he drifted away again.

Zeke sent me Interflora flowers with a note that read, 'You'll need these more than he does, Annie.'

# 33

As fit as he was before the operation, it took Doug all of his three months' sick leave to recover his energy.

Alex was our staunchest support during these months. He came round every day and they'd go out walking, a short way at first, after which Doug would return home shaky and needing a cup of sweet tea to revive his spirits. The walks grew longer as he felt better, and he also began to exercise in the club gym, saying, 'Might as well use the available facilities.'

Robin had taken leave from his vac job and flown down to see Doug after the operation. I'd driven him to the hospital and sat outside the ward watching through the open door and listening to their stilted conversation.

'How are you, Dad, feeling better?'

'Somewhat.' Turning his head away as if he couldn't bear to see his son weather-beaten like a Celtic warrior after a long campaign.

'I'm glad. Want me to come again?'

'If you like.'

'I said, do you want me to come again?'

An indifferent shrug. 'Up to you.'

Robin came out fuming. 'He treats me as if I'm a dog turd he's picked up on his shoe and is trying to scrape off.'

'Dad's not good at being ill,' I pleaded in a whisper. 'Give him time.'

'Bugger that. I'm not begging for his attention. Too busy. I'll come and see you again when he's gone back to work.'

'If, not when.'

I was fishing for sympathy but my answer from Robin was a cynical snort. 'Oh, he'll go back even if he has to crawl. His pride depends on it.'

Walking with him towards the car, I prayed that Doug hadn't heard. Gone was the sixth-form schoolboy who had lived for cricket and girls. In his place was a serious student who had moved on to study agricultural economics. Back home over supper, he lectured us about crop yields and the influence of farming subsidies on exports. When the twins teasingly asked about his love life, he said it was non-existent, adding, 'If I'm not studying, I'm working damn hard on farms. I want to show Dad he was wrong.'

Striving, I thought, just like his father. They were so alike in their stubborn drivenness to succeed, though Robin was not as anxious. I hoped that he'd inherited some of my optimism and wouldn't be plagued by bad luck – if Doug's misfortunes were bad luck and not just the negative karma of having to live with a successful wife, as he had half convinced me.

The surgeon didn't consider chemotherapy necessary, so Doug was spared the debilitation that went with it. That time, at least. After two months he was able to row again on the lake and began to cheer up. By the time he was ready to go back to work, he seemed almost his old self: thinner and less ebullient, but keen to resume his schedule.

The surgeon gave him the all-clear at three months and the estate committee welcomed him back with a cocktail party in the clubhouse for Rigby Vale residents. I stood with Alex watching him as he worked the room, engaging people in chats punctuated by the genial laughter required of the captains of cruise ships.

'He looks well,' Alex said.

'Says he feels great.'

'And does he?' I got the diplomatic raised eyebrow.

'I think so, but there's apprehension. He's dreading his next PSA test. You know Doug: he never expects his luck to last.'

Alex chuckled. 'Just so. Always was a morbid sort.'

'Even at Oxford?' This was a surprise. I'd been there at Oxford working on the newspaper and never thought of him as morbid.

'Used to talk about striving all the time, quoting that turgid Tennyson piece so beloved by Victorians.' He struck a pose with one hand raised. '"That which we are, we are; / One equal temper of heroic hearts, / Made weak by time and fate, but strong in will / To strive, to seek, to find, and not to yield." I thought it was hopelessly outdated compared with existentialism.'

'That was his father speaking,' I said, leaping to Doug's defence.

'I know. Mine tried to inculcate his favourite maxims too,

but I had crucial battles to fight – he loathed and despised queers – and my resistance was tougher than Doug's.' His tone changed as he said in a lower voice, 'I fear for him now, Annie. He's been battered too often.'

I'd never have confessed to anyone that Doug and I were having problems because he felt that his manhood had been taken away. So I just said, 'Me too. This last setback has hit him harder than ever.'

Alex nodded. 'And you're getting it in the neck again.'

'How did you—?'

'Know? Been there. Geoffrey was a pessimist too. I think it lurks in the genes, if that's any comfort. And it's extraordinarily hard to live with the constant drip of self-doubt, even when you truly love your partner. Just remember that I'm here if you need help. Right?'

'Right. Thanks. You're a wonderful friend.' I squeezed his hand.

'I'd like to think I am,' he said sadly, 'though I haven't succeeded as a lover.'

For the next few months our lives seemed back on track. Doug was up and around, active as ever. In our bubble of white privilege, insulated from the continuing mayhem in the streets and townships, we had good times with Alex and friends we'd made on the estate. Most of the residents were retirees who played bowls or golfers with bored wives who hung around the clubhouse, but there were a few who'd bought into Rigby Vale after interesting careers.

Making love had become an ordeal, however. What had

once been a joyous romp became a fretful business of, 'Can we try now?' followed by struggles that often ended in failure.

'You'd be justified in leaving me,' he said once, late at night after we'd tried to make something – anything – happen and were lying side by side staring up at the ceiling.

I turned and stared at him. 'Why would I do that?'

'You have conjugal rights which I can't provide. That's grounds for divorce in a court of law.'

It was the self-pity that made me furious. 'I didn't marry you for conjugal rights! We enjoyed those beforehand, remember? I married you because I loved you and wanted to spend my life with you.'

'And now? Do you still love this pathetic farce of a husband?'

'Very much. When you're not feeling sorry for yourself.'

'Not all the time? Now, for example?' His eyes were flakes of slate.

And I said, 'Not right now.'

'A true confession at last. Sorry I can't pleasure you.'

'You don't have to keep apologising.' I sat up and pulled the sheet round me, thinking, It's time to have things out. 'I thought that coming to Rigby Vale had healed old wounds, but this surgery seems to have hacked them wide open. It's me who can't please you. Admit it.'

'No, Annie!' He grabbed my hand. 'That's not so. You've been a wonderful wife. Superior on all counts. I'm the failure.'

'Stop it.' I flung him away and got up and stood by the bed. 'I'm sick and tired of hearing you whine about failure. You're the kingpin of this place and we've been a bloody successful partnership. Just grow up!'

Steeling myself against the tears that welled in his eyes, I put on my dressing gown and went out slamming the door. Doug didn't follow after a while, as he usually did when we fought. By the time I'd made myself a consoling mug of hot Milo in the kitchen, watched some TV as I sipped it and gone back to bed, he was asleep with his back turned.

When I pulled the sheet up over his shoulders, the hem was wet.

My highlights that year were the twins dropping by on brief visits, and once when Robin was in Cape Town on a course and came to see me when he knew his father would be out. The gulf between them continued despite Robin's string of firsts in the June exams. All Doug had said was, 'I know he isn't stupid. That's why I was so bloody mad when he turned down UCT. You've got to grab a good offer because it may not happen again.'

Robin was alight with missionary zeal as he told me how pesticides contaminate our rivers and groundwater, and that too many domestic animals are dosed with hormones.

'Farmers need scientific expertise to combat the long-term fertilising and irrigation crusting the soil with salts. On the plus side, my profs are saying that genetic modifications will revolutionise food production in poor countries. They're the hope of the world.'

'What's happened to the organic farming you were so keen on? People say GM food is dangerous,' I bleated.

'Rubbish, Mum. There's nothing unnatural about modifying genes to improve crops. That's one of the reasons why I'm focusing on scientific developments, to advance farming in South Africa.'

'But wasn't your whole idea to work in the open air?'

'Got carried away,' he admitted. 'I've learnt so much more now. Research and economics are as important as practical stuff like learning to plough and helping sows to farrow. They're all vital skills and I love every moment of what I'm doing. Grandpa understands.'

My father was a man of his time who pooh-poohed psychology, but he understood Robin in a way that Doug never could. Robin still went fishing with his grandfather – there are wonderful trout waters in Du Toit's Kloof and near Worcester – though he remained hands-off with his father.

'He thinks I chose an easy option because I was too pigheaded to listen to his words of wisdom.'

'No he doesn't,' I lied.

'You don't have to worry about my feelings,' said the scientist who had emerged from the chrysalis of the would-be farmer. 'I know he's projecting his problems onto me. I can handle it. A lot of my friends have the same trouble. Just be straight with me yourself, okay? I want to know the truth about his condition. Tell me.'

In the usual way of mothers, I'd given the children an edited version of Doug's situation. Robin was demanding to be treated as an adult now.

I said, 'The surgeon thinks he got all the cancer, but' – this bit was hard – 'Dad's impotent. For the time being, anyway.

That's the worst thing for him. And of course he's frightened about future tests.'

'Oh.' Robin blinked; impotence had never crossed his mind. Then he said, 'Thanks, Mum. I'll try to be more understanding.'

Besides me, he was impressing his professors. They suggested that he research drip irrigation networks for an MSc and offered a bursary, preceded by an intensive course on an Israeli kibbutz. He came home bubbling with enthusiasm for the way of life.

'The Israelis are so laidback. No airs and graces. No false modesty.' He slid me a sideways look. 'No harping on about striving. They don't have any small talk, just roll up their sleeves and get stuck in.'

I just wished Doug could see his son through other eyes. Why is it that we extrapolate our worst misgivings onto our children, instead of listening to them? From the time Robin turned sixteen there'd been a disquieting thrum of competition between him and Doug that began when Robin first beat him in a single sculls race. Perhaps that was the reason why the Austin 6 had been abandoned to dust and cobwebs? Doug was the loser. As Robin drove away I made a wish that time would heal the breach, unaware how little time was left.

Dad had even less. He died of a heart attack brought on by the stress of fighting and landing a record brown trout. When a friend drove him home curled up in pain on the back seat of his car, he greeted Mum with a shaky smile and said, 'I let the damn fish get away.'

Robin quoted Dad's favourite Ralph Waldo Emerson when he gave the eulogy at his funeral, standing tall and tanned in front of the altar and speaking with the easy confidence of a young man who knows where he is going.

I stole a sideways look at Doug, saw that there were tears in his eyes again, and hoped with all my heart that they were of pride and not apprehension.

# 34

Beyond the problems simmering under the surface of our lives, 1993 was an increasingly tense year as the advisability of the decision to return to South Africa hung in the balance. The brutal murder of Chris Hani just before Easter and continuing social turmoil meant that the fears about Doug's condition were compounded by anxiety over our children's future.

'At least they can go back to England if they want to,' he said several times. 'They're British citizens.'

'So are we.'

'Leaving is out of the question for us.' End of discussion as his mouth clamped down.

Soldiering on with new handbooks kept me occupied. But Philisa was only coming in once a week now, and without her lively gossip about her family's misdeeds – 'Those tsotsi boys of mine, hawu!' – the house was too quiet. I found myself longing for the bustle of hungry kids, Budgie cussing in the kitchen, and the sound of Lally's receiver crashing down on another demand.

Budgie and my English friends and I kept in touch by phoning on special occasions like birthdays, but long-distance was too expensive to call often.

Cuckoo had moved to Great Ormonde Street, where she was in charge of the high care unit for premature babies with multiple complications. She had no time for men, she said, except for what she called 'essential services'.

Susie was a lively source of London gossip during our brief chats, though ever-busy with her kids and working in Xavier's practice. He had become the sought-after architect for conversions of old industrial buildings to loft apartments, a new trend that was grist to Lally's *Modern* mill. I'd had no contact with Lally since our acrimonious farewell and never heard from Ginger, who had moved to *Vogue* in New York.

I see her photo sometimes on the social pages of waiting room magazines. In her cocktail finery of glistening scales, she looks even more like an exotic fish.

There was only one call from Vron, who was seeing a married man – which seemed to have become a habit. 'Divorce makes you wary of getting permanently involved,' she said, 'especially with guys who expect you to do everything for them.' In the manner of old friends, we still exchanged birthday cards with brief cheery messages, though she didn't call again. Cuckoo, who saw her sometimes for coffee, told me that she was becoming solitary. 'She says she has to be discreet because her lover is an important man who can't afford negative publicity, but I think her life has narrowed down to him and her work. It's so sad.'

Budgie faxed some of the rave reviews for her spy thriller.

'Didn't think I had it in me,' she crowed before posting us a copy. 'Writing about spies was bloody good fun too. Dodgy business, though.'

'Writing?'

'Letting out secrets about Century House, where I worked. Terrible publicity for MI6.' She gave a hoot of delight. 'My old friends reckon the bosses are furious. Hue and cry everywhere. Publishers want three more.'

'Old friends' was her euphemism for the former colleagues she met sometimes in the City. No wonder she had used a pen name.

'They haven't found out who Victor B is yet?'

'Know how to cover my tracks. You don't know the effing half of it. I can turn myself into a gullible shopper in a flash, for instance little old Wilma Budge, dithery pensioner.'

I pictured her screwing up her face and putting on a simpering, toothy smile and had to laugh. She'd always been there when we needed her: helper, friend, critic, chief cook, and a fund of common sense. Budgie was a treasure who lightened my life for years.

Planning for my last book began without an inkling of its potential for mayhem. *True Blue Superglue* was conceived as a tribute to marriage, though I nearly destroyed it by writing a self-improvement handbook that tempted fate.

Mum said when I finally told her, 'You've forgotten that the pen is mightier than the sword.'

Older readers will remember Anne Perceval, wife and mother, food expert and trusted counsellor. As a founding freelancer on *Modern Lifestyle*, I'd worked from home for decades writing about cooking and giving advice on personal problems, trumpeting that a home-based career was the best option for mothers who wanted to be *there* for their kids. The readers believed that I was a woman who had it all.

I thought so too for most of my marriage.

But I was wrong. However well working wives learn to juggle our many commitments, the strain of keeping all those balls in the air requires remorseless effort that inevitably gnaws at relationships.

Doug used to say, 'I'm the long-suffering uncle stuck with the agony aunt, ha ha.' It started as a joke.

With the world heading for the end of another millennium, I wanted to write about something that was important to me but seemed to have gone out of fashion: fidelity. It would be a belated silver anniversary gift to Doug. From our new home by the Rigby Vale lake, I would radiate the ethos of a woman whose life had been blessed by a long and faithful relationship.

But a disclaimer before describing my folly: motivational literature has a particular tone which I'd perfected. The handbook publisher told all his authors before they began, 'I don't want beautiful prose. I don't want long-winded opinions or patronising advice. I want a gung-ho guru who speaks from the heart. Short, punchy and believable. Optimism sells. Bring in sex as soon as possible.'

When I proposed fidelity as a long-ignored virtue that needed reviving, he suggested the catchy title, reinforced by a strap-line to attract his target audience, people who believed that an x-factor could transform lives. 'TRUE BLUE SUPERGLUE!

The power source of successful relationships' it blared in raised silver lettering on a rich royal blue.

The opening page read:

***Introduction***

*Want to enrich and add value to your life? Achieve impressive stability? Establish rewarding partnerships?*

*The power source of all these things is no secret: it's fidelity. Yup, good old-fashioned loyalty. It's the reason why marriages last, great friends become old friends, fortunate kids know they can depend on their parents, and dogs are sometimes called Fido.*

*Because trust is the vital ingredient in relationships – all kinds, from lovemaking to business deals, teaching to teamwork – and fidelity is the key component of trust. We feel confident and safe with someone who can be trusted, which encourages us to aim further and higher. Launched from firm ground, we can soar.*

*This book is in praise of fidelity, and I know what I'm talking about because I've only had one lover in my life – and I've been married to him for nearly twenty-nine years. If that doesn't convince you that fidelity is worth striving for, nothing will!*

It's appalling in retrospect. So smug. So pleased with myself. I truly believed when I wrote this that Doug's and my relationship was at the high end of the scale.

After all our years together I thought I knew everything about him, and I didn't. We'd both changed and I continued to deny it. Gliding along on the wings of my lucrative career, I'd thought of myself as the backroom provider who underpinned his efforts, not – as he later accused – an emasculating queen bee who ignored his struggles mired in the honey-trap of our marriage and devoured his will to succeed.

But I was blind, not devouring. And he was never a drone.

Towards the end of that year Nelson Mandela and the president who had released him at last, FW de Klerk, were awarded the Nobel Peace Prize, which cheered everyone as a good omen for the first democratic election. We managed to get through a family Christmas with the children home for a few days and grandparents visiting, all of us being ultra-polite to each other.

But Doug had only seven more months in the sunshine before his PSA began to rocket.

# 35

After the years of unrest and fears when many families packed up and left, scurrying away from the prophecies of disaster, the lead-up to the election was nerve-racking. People stockpiled tinned goods in preparation for a siege. Shop windows emptied. Army units were deployed in long convoys of khaki trucks to set up camp in public spaces. Rigby Vale estate beefed up its security and Doug sent round circulars urging everyone to make sure they laid in fuel supplies and had plenty of available cash in case the banks closed. The twins came home to vote with us while Robin voted in Maritzburg, where he was putting down roots, he said. Philisa was given a fortnight off so she could travel to the Transkei to be with her family.

All the angst fizzled out on the day when people stood in endless good-natured queues at the polling stations. The peace lasted into the second and subsequent days of joyful celebrations until the transcendent moment when President Mandela took the oath at the Union Buildings, followed by the fly-past of helicopters dangling our bright new flag promising better times for all.

Though not for us. Doug's post-op scan had been clear and his six-month and one-year PSA tests were normal. We began to think he was out of the woods. But the eighteen-month test showed an ominous rise. The urologist phoned him with the result and said he'd have to start radiation treatment at once, followed by at least one course of chemotherapy. I was in the room when Doug took the call, and saw him go pale and collapse into a chair. I rushed over. 'What's wrong?'

'Urologist says my PSA's shot up. Surgery can release cancer cells into the lymphatic system.' He looked stunned.

'But the surgeon said—'

'The urologist told me that there were no guarantees.'

He hadn't mentioned this and I felt my blood run cold. The urologist was an arrogant medical snob who'd insisted on consulting Doug alone and refused to answer my questions in the waiting room after the operation, saying that the matter was between him and his patient.

'I'm his wife!' I'd shouted in exasperation.

'Ask him, then.' Cold as a witch's tit, as Budgie would put it.

When I asked him, Doug had said, 'Oh, it went off all right.'

I'd been left out of the decisions and the outcome – a male conspiracy that enraged me. What is it about doctors that makes them think they're gods dispensing health to lesser mortals? And why do people facing fatal illnesses feel they have to protect their families from the truth? We want to know the worst so we can prepare ourselves. But I hadn't come even close to the worst yet.

I won't go into the details of his radiation therapy, slow recovery at home and then the shock of learning after another scan that several tumours had showed up in his bladder.

The surgeon wanted to do a trans-urethral resection, saying, 'I think we could catch those strays if we act now and follow up the procedure with two courses of chemo.' He had come round his desk and was sitting on an easy chair next to me, leaning towards Doug. 'I've had good results from that combination.'

'What do you mean by "good"? Fifty per cent survival? More?'

'We never talk per centages. We concentrate on individual patients. You're basically a fit man, Mr Perceval. No reason why you can't beat this thing.'

I was watching Doug, willing him to grab the straw being offered, and I saw his neck flush an angry purplish red. He said in a thick voice, 'This thing? Those strays? Why do you keep using euphemisms? It's cancer, goddammit! Cancer. Be straight with me. This is my life on the line.'

The surgeon, unfazed, said gently, 'And I'm doing my best to help you maintain that life in good health. Cancer is daunting, but we're winning more battles against it every year. The prognosis for prostate cancer if caught early, as yours was, is generally optimistic.'

'But not if it has begun to spread?'

The surgeon avoided a direct answer. 'We have excellent weapons to fight it if you agree to—'

'I won't have surgery again.'

'Very well. I'll refer you to an oncologist with the recommendation that he starts chemo right away.'

Doug's bones were beginning to jut out of his face, which had lost its tan during the weeks of radiation. He was also racked by anxiety over his job. The estate committee chairman had said that of course they'd hold it and the house for him as long as necessary, of *course,* he was indispensable.

'I don't believe him,' Doug muttered as I drove him to the oncology unit at Groote Schuur. 'The last person they want running a high-status operation like Rigby Vale is a sick man. I know the form. They'll offer me a package to get rid of me. We're going to lose the house too. This is Armageddon.' He added in that thick voice, 'Best we drive up to Chapman's Peak and off the edge.'

'Forget it,' was all I could manage before it all began. The reclining chairs, the ever-so-kind nurses, the needles, the drips, the anti-nausea medication, the cups of weak sweet tea, and later, the smaller and smaller sips of water. He felt all right after the first few treatments but worsened as the therapy progressed. After the last session, he had to be pushed out to the car in a wheelchair and carried to the sofa by Alex when we got home.

The two weeks of treatments dragged into a month before he began to feel better. I nursed him like an ailing child, tempting him with morsels of food and small glasses of freshly-squeezed fruit juice. Alex came often to chat, or just sit with him by the window looking down the lawn to the lake. The twins came every weekend, though there were no calls from Robin. I knew that the three of them kept in touch, but also that they wouldn't betray each other's confidences. If he didn't want to come and see his father, it was his decision.

There's a limit to buttoned lips, however. 'Where is Robin?' I demanded during a confab at home while Doug was having his last treatment.

Tasha answered. 'He's got a vac job on some big hydroponic scheme in the Free State. It's a tunnel farm.'

'Does he know about the chemo?'

'Yes. We tell him everything.' Chloe gave me her duh look.

'He could come and see for himself.'

'He tried after the operation and at Christmas, remember?' Tasha got up and stood in front of where I was sitting. 'Why is Dad so adamant about him?'

'It's a father–son thing,' I said feebly.

'It's bloody nonsense.' Chloe stood next to her sister. 'Robin's doing brilliantly at university. Dad has no right to keep on holding a grudge just because he didn't study law or something equally irrelevant to him.'

'It's mediaeval.'

'And you've got to do something about it.'

'Soon. What if Dad gets worse?'

'He's a lot better this week,' I said.

Both my girls looked down at me with pitying expressions that said they couldn't believe the folly of the aged.

'You're in denial, Mum,' Chloe said.

'He looks awful,' Tasha whispered.

'Awful.' Chloe began crying.

We sat hugging each other in silent tears. When they could talk again, the twins made me promise to try to mend the rift.

'Even if you have to threaten both of them. It's your job as a mother, to fix things,' Tasha said.

'I'll tell Robin to phone you next time he calls.' Chloe raised her clenched fist. 'Women's solidarity, okay?'

'Okay.'

She looked so touchingly young to call herself a woman, yet they had both matured in their first year away from home. We weren't to call them 'the twins' any more; they were individuals, Tasha and Chloe. Remembering how grown-up and responsible I'd felt going off to university, it was hard not to smile.

Now I dried my eyes, thinking, Is it my job as a mother to fix things? Yes. Am I in denial? Yes. Are we downhearted? No. Well, yes. In my heart I knew that Doug was fighting what could be a final battle. And Robin would never forgive himself if he didn't patch things up with the father he loved, but who couldn't show how much he loved him.

Alex helped me, dear Alex, the pillar of the family in that bleak year. He sent a message via Chloe that he had arranged an air ticket for Robin to come home and see Doug. Robin could be as stubborn as his father and then some, but I think a panic button was pressed. Alex went to fetch him at the airport and I was to prepare Doug for their arrival.

He sat in his usual place by the window, gazing down at the lake with the intensity of an artist trying to capture a scene on canvas. I've often seen that look on Mum's face.

'Penny for your thoughts.'

'Regret,' he mumbled. 'Disappointment that I didn't make it.'

'But you're feeling better, aren't you? The doctors say—'

'What do they know? Bugger all. I'm finished. Up shit creek without a paddle.'

I went and knelt down in front of him. 'Not yet, Doug! You've got to fight this … cancer.' He got furious when people said 'this thing'.

There was no anger now. His eyes were full of tears, the wet slate I remembered so well. 'I'm weary, Annie. Old Man River, he's sick of trying. Tired of living. Scared of dying.'

*Oh God.* He was giving up. To cover my panic, I said, 'That's the wrong song. Remember the wartime one that Mum and Dad used to sing, "Ac-Cent-Tchu-Ate the Positive"?'

Doug managed a faint smile. 'Describes me exactly: Mister In-Between.'

I leant forward to stroke his face. 'That's not true. You're the wonderful, irreplaceable, ever-supportive rock in my life. This family revolves round you. You're our mainstay.'

'Mainstay, hell. The family's gone. It's down to the two of us.'

I seized the opportunity and said, 'Not only the two of us. Alex is bringing Robin to see you this afternoon.'

His response was derision. 'Ah, young Farmer Brown. All cocky with his tractor licence and a yard of shit up his arm from inseminating cows. Make sure he has a good wash before he ventures in to comfort the sick. My immune system isn't what it was.'

It was the strongest response I'd had from him in weeks. He'd drive our son away with sarcasm and Robin would fling out of the house, vowing not to come back. What was it with men – pride? Control? Fear of competition? All I wanted for our children was that they'd be happy in the work they chose, but Doug's disappointments had distorted his vision. He saw only the possibility of Robin trying and failing as he had – and even worse, at work he considered inferior. August old universities like Oxford cast long shadows.

I thought, How would Quince handle this? Persuasion, she'd say. Make him see Robin's point of view. Jolt him into it, if necessary.

I said, 'That's unfair, Doug. You know that he's researching the design of drip irrigation networks. It's complex work timed with computers.'

'Wow, my son the drip irrigator. Or should I just say, the drip?'

Doug's face was twisted in mockery. It made me mad. I grabbed his shoulders and shook them. 'You're so stupid! This is your only son. Listen to him. Show him some respect.'

'Like he listened to me? Respected my wishes?'

'He listened, Doug. He did. And he chose a different route. It was simply his preference, not a reflection on you. He loves you.'

'He's got a funny way of showing it.'

I dropped my hands to squeeze his cold ones. 'He'll be here any minute. Try and be nice to him. He's worried about you.'

'I'm worried about me.'

'Please make an effort. Robin needs your approval.' What else could I say? It was my job as a mother to fix things. I said, 'Do you remember when he used to throw all the keys out the window? He was such a busy little boy. So curious. So affectionate.'

'That was a long time ago. He'll think I'm pathetic now. Wreck of the *Hesperus*. How the mighty have fallen.'

I trembled inside at his despair, but managed to say, 'Not fallen. Just catching up again.'

'Fallen,' Doug said in a broken whisper.

I heard Alex's car coming up the drive and squeezed his hands again. 'Here they are. Give Robin time for what he needs to say. Promise? He's really trying. He loves you.'

Doug gave me a wordless nod and I got up to welcome the arrivals. Robin went in to see his father alone while I hovered with Alex in the kitchen. Hoping and praying, if silent pleas to the gods of family togetherness count. All three of us had been young in the fifties when togetherness was a good thing, not the butt of jokes as it is today. When sons still wondered how to stand up to their fathers, and daughters were on the threshold of extraordinary new freedoms.

Alex said in his droll way, 'Alors, we 'ope for ze best, eh?'

And his plan worked. Robin came out after a while saying, 'Dad and I would like some tea, please.' His face was stern, but no longer angry.

'Of course. I'll make some.'

'He looks terrible. Broken. Why, Mum? He was so strong.'

'I don't know.' I put my arms round him and we hugged our sorrow, holding back tears that would upset Doug again.

But he managed a smile when we went in with the tea, enjoying the irony as he said, 'I'm glad you came home, my dear boy. Thank you for swallowing my pride.'

# 36

Our lives unravelled after the second course of chemotherapy. Exhausted by the final session, Doug lay on the sofa by the window all afternoon, alternately dozing and looking down at the lake. I tiptoed in and out with glasses of water, though he wouldn't drink anything.

'Please, love. You need to keep up your fluids.'

'Can't. I'd bring it up.'

'Shall I fetch a straw so you can sip?'

'No.' He turned his face away.

Later I covered him with a blanket and slept fitfully on the other sofa.

Next morning he felt a bit better and I helped him into the shower, fresh pyjamas and back to the sofa, then brought a small glass of iced tea sweetened with honey. 'Get some of this down. It'll keep up your strength.'

He shook his head, holding out trembling hands. 'What strength? Shadow of my former self.'

I said, half-joking, 'That was an order, not a request.'

He gave a weak salute. 'Always at the helm, Captain Annie.'

'Please just try some.'

'Aye, aye, sir. Or should I say madam?' His gaunt face was twisted in a mocking rictus.

I went away to shed the tears he didn't want to see. There would be many more before the end of that day and the terrible weeks that followed.

A proof copy of *True Blue Superglue* arrived by courier that afternoon. In my final throes of innocence, I thought that Doug would be cheered by the tribute I'd written to celebrate our marriage. After I'd opened it and checked the dedication and acknowledgement pages, I took it to him saying, 'Here's my new book.'

'Oh.' He lay watching a rugby match on TV and didn't turn his head.

'I wrote it to thank you.'

'For what?'

'All our years together. You've made me so happy.'

He looked up at me now, dull eyes in a chalky face. 'Been more of a burden than a source of boundless joy.'

'That's not true. We've had a lovely life together, the two of us and the children. You've just had some bad spells.'

'I let you down.' His hands trembled on the rug over his knees. 'You should have married someone more accomplished.'

'It was always you, never anyone else.' I knelt down and gave him the proof copy. 'This is my tribute.'

He turned it over and glanced at the cover. 'True blue superglue? Some weird magic formula for people on a quest for self-improvement? Poor suckers.'

'No, it's about fidelity. The joys of being faithful to each other all these years. My thank you is in the dedication.'

I sat back on my heels expecting him to open it and read what I'd written: 'For DP, my soul mate: after twenty-nine years, a million thanks.'

But he didn't. He looked at me for the longest time, then said, 'Fidelity is fine as an ideal but hard to maintain in the real world.'

'What?' It sounded all wrong.

'Men are different. It's common knowledge.' He raised one bony finger like a prophet laying down the law, and the proof copy slid to the floor.

'Rule number one in the sexual equation: never underestimate the power of the balls.'

'Doug?' I grabbed his shoulders and shook them as though he were a child who needed to be punished for lying. 'What are you saying?'

'Only what you've been trying to explain in your so-helpful columns and booklets all these years. Men like to be in charge, to assert our masculinity, Annie. Not only when we're young and strong, but when we get older and desperate to keep the failing pecker active.'

'But I didn't mean you. I meant—'

'Other men. Not your incompetent husband.'

His words coiled round my chest like a python, squeezing out my breath so I couldn't speak as my hands fell away.

He went on stabbing words at me. 'You assumed I was some kind of eunuch? Even before the op?'

Of course I hadn't. I'd thought our love was mutual. I didn't know how to answer this belligerent alien who had taken over my husband's body.

'Did you? Did you?' he demanded.

'Of course not,' I managed to whisper. 'We were so good together.'

'We were, before I started going downhill. Then I needed more. I needed to be successful too. To make my own conquests.'

'But I never refused you.'

The alien said, 'Not exactly. You fitted me in when it suited you, the busy queen bee involved in your work and the children. Cooking up something for Zeke to photograph and millions of women to gush over. Clever Annie Butterfield, diligent adviser of the upwardly mobile, the problem-riddled and the housebound. You hardly noticed when I wasn't there.'

'That's not true!' I went on in a desperate gabble. 'I loved it when you came home. I loved the sight of you in the door, and the smell of you when your arms went round me. I've loved you since the day we met. Only you. I've never looked at another man that way.'

'*That way*,' he mocked. 'You sound like a Victorian.'

I sat back on my heels and wrapped my arms round my chest to protect my heart, which felt as though it was going to burst with sorrow. 'I thought you loved me. Only me.'

He pushed himself up on the cushions to half-sitting, saying, 'For god's sake, you're making too much of this. Of course I love you, but it wasn't enough. I'm an imperfect man, not a paragon of virtue.'

I couldn't look at him. 'I thought the love we had was sacred.'

His laugh was short and hard. 'Can't say I ever thought of it as a sacrament. Bloody good fun, though. You've been a good wife. Good in bed and a damn good provider. I just haven't been the husband you imagined.'

It was the laugh that began the rot.

'How can you say these things?'

'Tried to tell you I wasn't perfect. Often. You weren't listening. All these years you've lived inside your smug little bubble, impervious to what I needed because I wasn't a reader asking for advice.'

I had to hold my body to contain my growing fury. 'I thought you were just unlucky. Kept making excuses while—'

'Illusion,' he cut in. 'You always were a cock-eyed optimist.'

And he always took the darker view. 'One of us has to keep watch for storm clouds,' had been a constant refrain. All the girls in my year at university had fancied him, and I'd been so proud to be the one he chose. Had it been because I was the most likely to allow him to 'do it', at that time when nice girls didn't? Available Annie, naïve to a fault. Double fault.

I flared, 'But I believed in you! In being faithful.'

'And you've kept me in style all these years. Pity I wasn't able to play my part in the impossible contract you had in mind.'

'You bastard!'

He gave me a caustic smile. 'What I did with other women was just sex. A bonk here and there, nothing serious. No long-term involvements. Knew I'd have to confess one day. What better time than now, when I feel like shit anyway?'

'Other women. Just sex. What did we have, then?'

'A marriage, of course. Sex with all the accoutrements.'

I turned away from the ugly, bruising words and got up and left him. For the rest of that day and all night I kept holding and rocking my body, but the agony and rage went on and on. I lay grieving and furious on our bed and he lay on the sofa, both of us mute. Even when Alex came by and went back and forth between us, trying to understand what had happened.

On the afternoon of the second day he called the twins home, hoping they'd talk sense into us, though didn't tell them what he suspected. Alex knew how to keep secrets.

# 37

Tasha and Chloe came early next morning and Robin flew home later that day, hiring a car at the airport. Alex had advised them not to involve Mum and told them only that it was an emergency situation, with the two of us not speaking to each other after a major disagreement, he wasn't sure why.

They came to the bedroom in relays to bombard me with questions.

'What is it? What's wrong? Is Dad dying? Why aren't you talking? What's wrong?'

'Can't say.' My eyelids were so swollen that I could hardly see through them. I was still in pyjamas and couldn't keep food down. Alex had been forcing me to drink water.

'Speak to us!' Robin demanded. 'What's going on? All Dad says is, "Ask your mother."'

'You don't want to know.' I turned my back and sobbed.

'How can you do this to him when he's so sick?' each one accused me, but I couldn't answer. What was there to say? That their father had been having affairs with other women and I'd only just found out? That no one could be trusted, not even one's nearest and dearest? That men were bastards? Doug may have betrayed me but I wasn't going to damage our children's trust in him. Mothers can hold the faith even if philandering fathers can't.

After an hour of this Robin phoned Mum. I heard his voice in the hallway, high with anxiety. 'You've got to come, Gran! There's something terribly wrong here. The parents aren't talking to each other. It's like a morgue.'

There was silence while he listened to her answer, then, 'Just come quickly. We need you.'

Deep in my fog of misery I wondered how long it would take for her to unbutton her smock, cover her paints, hang the old sheet she used over the current painting, wash her hands, change into clean clothes, lock up the house and drive out at her usual leisurely pace … Half an hour flat, it took. So even Mum was worried. I heard a mumble of voices and her steps hurrying to my room. She closed the door before coming to sit next to me on the bed.

'Annie, what's wrong?'

'Can't say.'

'Tell me. The children are beside themselves.'

'They mustn't know.' I couldn't look at her.

'What mustn't they know?' She put a hand on my shoulder. 'Is Doug dying? He won't let any of us near him.'

'I wish he would die.'

There was a considering silence, then Mum said, 'Is he the one in pain, or are you?'

'Me. I don't care if he is any more.'

'What has he done? Tell me.'

'I can't. It's too humiliating.'

Her arms came round me and she picked me up and held me against her shoulder as she had when I was a small girl. 'Come on, darling. Tell your old Mum.'

'I'll never forgive the shit!'

'Ah.' More silence, then, 'He's told you that he had an affair.'

I pulled away and looked at her. 'How do you know?'

She shrugged. 'I don't. I'm guessing. He's a very attractive man, Annie.'

'Was. Now he's pathetic. And it wasn't one affair.'

'Several?'

I put my head back on her shoulder and mumbled into it. 'I don't know how many. He said I was always busy and that men like to be in charge. To assert their masculinity.' I couldn't stop now. 'Just sex, he said. Nothing serious. No long-term involvements. He said that he isn't a paragon of virtue.'

'Is that all?'

'No. He also said that I should never underestimate the power of the balls. Like it wasn't his fault, just his hormones.'

Mum said after a while, 'Par for the course.'

I jerked back to look at her face. 'What?'

She lifted me up so we were sitting facing each other and took my hands. 'Listen to me, Annie. Men stray. They seem to get so overwhelmed by their physical needs that they lose all reason and grab a willing woman without a thought for the consequences. I've seen it explained as ego-boosting temporary madness.'

'That's no excuse.'

'It's an explanation. Politicians are specially prone. Look at Bill Clinton. John Profumo. John Major, for heaven's sake. Just think what they stood to lose for a few hours of—'

'Fun?'

'I was going to say nookie. More furtive.'

'Doug isn't a politician. And I supported him for so long.' I felt my gorge rising again. 'How dare he run off and do things with other women while I was slaving away for our family?'

Mum said quietly, 'Are you aware of what you've just said?'

'Of course I am! Whose side are you on?'

'Both. I've watched your marriage from the beginning: the good times, the strains, the doldrums. I've seen you thriving on your success and Doug finding it hard to swallow.'

'That wasn't my fault.'

I tried to pull my hands back, angry at the way she was trying to exonerate him, but Mum hung on to them.

'Just listen for a moment, Annie. I've seen this happen with some of my friends. Like Dad—'

'Dad too?'

'If you count fish as femmes fatales. I was trying to say that like Dad, Doug belongs to a generation who thought it was their duty to get a steady job so they could make a home for their families. Very fifties. He felt disempowered when his jobs folded. And the best way to counteract that feeling is to go out and wield power over someone else. Sex is one option. Violence is another.'

It could have been Quince talking. I said, ladling on the sarcasm, 'Spare me the psychology.'

Mum shook her head. 'Long experience, not psychology.

Surely Annie Butterfield had letters from betrayed wives in shock?'

'Plenty. But I never thought they'd apply to me.'

The unstoppable tears began again and she took out a wodge of tissues and handed them to me, saying as I mopped, 'Be grateful it wasn't more serious. Some husbands get so involved with other women – or men, for that matter – that they leave long-standing marriages for a fantasy, only to get dropped when someone better comes along. Happens to women too, though not as often because of their kids. Too many of these crises now. People are selfish today.' She seemed to go off into a brown study.

'Nobody could accuse me of being selfish,' I said bitterly. When she didn't answer, I shook her arm. 'Could they?'

I didn't often see her eyes behind her specs. Now they seemed to click back from the far place she had gone to and looked at me squarely over the rims. 'You're a good woman, certainly not selfish. Blinkered, perhaps.'

'Blinkered? That's a horrible thing to say.'

'Not really. Your writing demands it and I've learnt as an artist that I need time and absolute concentration to achieve what I'm aiming for. Did you never consider that Doug's needs could be as great or greater than the children's?'

'He didn't say anything.'

'My dear girl, men don't make overt emotional demands. They expect you to divine what they want.'

It felt strange, listening to this mother I'd written off long ago as an old fogey telling me stuff I hadn't learnt for myself in fifty years of living and more than two decades spent advising others how to cope with their problems. Maybe I was blinkered. But it didn't excuse Doug's betrayals.

I raged, 'I don't care what you say, he's a bastard. He let me down.'

'And now he's very ill.' Mum reached again for my hands as I had for Doug's in the past few months, trying to transmit fortitude. 'Forgive him for the past. It's the present that matters.'

'How can I? All these years I've thought he loved me. I thought he was faithful. I was.'

Doug's was the worst kind of betrayal, undermining my core belief that we'd had a good marriage. There'd been ups and downs along the way, but we'd been a team who complemented and supported each other, whatever problems we faced. During his bad times I'd sometimes wondered how my life might have turned out if I'd married someone else – dashing Rory the cricket captain, perhaps – but leaving Doug had never crossed my mind. He was my first and only lover, and I'd thought we were an ideal couple compared with most relationships.

My pride had been shattered as well as my illusions.

Mum was saying, 'He does love you, darling. And the children. He's a fine man. Just flawed, as we all are.'

'I thought we had the perfect marriage. How stupid I've been.'

'Is perfection more important to you than your marriage?'

That stopped me. Our marriage was between two people: Doug the striver who'd had so many disappointments and Annie the busy queen bee, too busy to listen to the problems he sweated over during his solitary rowing on the river. Why hadn't I noticed his distress signals? We had both made mistakes. We were both culpable. But his was the worse offence.

I said, 'Even if I'm partially at fault, it's no excuse. I can't forgive him.'

'Make a semblance for the children's sake? They're frantic with worry. And he looks completely drained.'

My mother knew how to push my buttons. She was right: the kids mustn't suffer and I could hardly turf Doug out when he was so ill. I thought, Bugger it, I'm trapped. It was a classic choice I'd advised so many of my readers to consider: if you have to decide between a hubby who's wronged you and the kids, don't punish the kids.

I said, grudgingly, 'I could try.'

Mum gathered me into a hug. 'It's going to be hard. You've had a devastating kick in the teeth. Just think how he must be feeling, to have hurt you like this.'

I mumbled into her shoulder, 'He seems glad, actually.'

'Confession is cathartic. He's relieved to have it out in the open.'

'No, it's like he's got me back at last for being more successful. As though he's been saying to himself all these years, Let her get caught up in her precious work, what do I care? I'll just go and fuck someone to spite her.'

'I know you're angry,' Mum began, 'but—'

'I'm not just angry, I'm fucking furious. I'm going to ask him who they were. I'm going to confront him.' I got up, threw off my pyjamas and began to pull on clothes. 'I have to know.'

Mum's hand clamped on my arm. 'Not now, Annie. Think

of the children. I'll make some tea while you reassure them, then we'll all behave like civilised beings and sit down together to enjoy it.'

'I can't,' I moaned.

The hand tightened. 'You can and you will. I demand it. Those three need some peace of mind when they leave. So does Alex. How you confront Doug afterwards is your business.'

'Bloody right.'

She shook my arm. 'Don't mow him down flat. Let him talk too. There's a better chance of healing if you discuss things rationally and—'

'No chance, Mum. Get that into your head. But okay, I'll reassure the kids and ask Alex to spend time chatting with Doug after they leave.'

'I'm not asking for the moon. Just listen to him.' She let me go and went to the door, adding, 'There may not be much time left. You'll regret it if you don't.' Mum was always good at exit lines.

I dressed and put on a face and went to tell Robin and Tasha and Chloe that Doug and I had had an argument, but we'd sort things out. Then I went through to Doug hunched on his sofa and hissed, 'Sit up now. We've got to put on a front for the kids. None of this is their fault.'

'Jesus, what a mess.'

The seducer I had married sat looking at me: grown old in a few months, unshaven, thin and shaky. The knave of hearts.

# 38

We managed the tea with stilted conversation and awkward silences. Then Mum invited the children to stay with her in Cape Town and they drove off in convoy. No doubt she'd fill them in about some of my deficiencies as she skirted round the real problem.

Damn it, I thought. Whatever Doug said about my being perpetually busy, my work had never taken precedence. On the contrary, it had been the safety net that kept us going during the times when he was unemployed and there were bills to pay. And he'd abused it by making whoopee with other women.

When Alex left too, I marched back to where he sat propped up with cushions, staring out the window, and thumped into a chair facing him. 'Okay. Now talk. Who were they?'

His face was grey and haggard, the deep frown knotting eyebrows that were threaded with tarnished silver wire like his hair.

He sighed, 'Not now.'

'Yes, now. You bloody owe it to me.'

'Do I?'

'Yes. I'm the injured party.'

'Funny, I thought I was.' He lifted his bony hands and looked at them. 'Couldn't even hold an oar now. Let alone an 'ore.'

I spoke through gritted teeth. 'Don't joke about it! I need to know.'

'Chapter and verse?'

'Starting from the first.'

'You were the first. You know that. Valiant Annie on my jacket in the long grass, allowing herself to be deflowered by a desperate youth who loved and needed her, then and there. I adored you.'

I could only nod. That's what I'd felt.

'Everyone says honeymoons don't last, but ours seemed to go on and on. All those good times in London when we sat in front of the gas fire dreaming dreams and talking about goals. We thought life was opening up for us, that we'd soon hit the highway to success. But we were green colonials without a clue.'

He fell silent, remembering. He looked so sad and defeated that I almost went to him, then thought, He's just trying to soften me up.

I said, 'And?'

'Then Robin came. And the twins. And Lally with her constant demands. Suddenly you were so busy that there wasn't time for just the two of us.'

'But you didn't say anything. I would have made time.'

'Maybe.'

'And Yselle was there to help. We could have got away on our own.'

Yselle Citron, our vivacious French au pair with dark curls and balsamic-brown eyes, who was so good with the twins. And Doug telling her, 'You're a beautiful person,' before she left in floods of tears.

I burst out, 'She was the first, wasn't she? Right there under my nose. Did you screw her on the table in the basement while I was working, or at night in her room when I was dead asleep with a twin on each side?'

He growled, 'Must you have all the details?'

'Every last sordid one. I want you to squirm.'

'Only when you were out,' he admitted, 'and only a few times. She understood.'

'What? That it was just sex?'

'That I needed – well, release. She did too.'

'Release! That's a new one. And was she a good fuck? Willing? Better than me?'

'I'm not going to answer that.' He clamped his mouth shut.

'Yes, you are. I insist.'

'No. I'll answer with bare facts because I feel guilty.'

'Very bare facts. Ha ha.'

He turned his tired face away.

'And I suppose Euphemia was next?'

'I wouldn't have dreamt of approaching Euphemia.'

'Racist.'

'No. She was self-sufficient. Strong. Not needy at all.'

'So that's your justification? It was needy women you went for?'

'I didn't "go for" anyone. I just responded to signals. Not often.'

'Only every now and again. I'm so relieved. Who was the next deprived soul, then?'

'Nerine. But she was before Yselle. She was the first.'

'Nerine?'

'The boss's PA. Very much a career woman. She initiated it. Said she wanted a man sometimes, without complications. I resisted at first, until she made it clear that she wouldn't make any other demands and ... well, I thought she'd chosen me as a promising executive.'

I remembered then: chic, willowy Nerine who had come to an early luncheon, the one for his work colleagues. I thought of the faint smile and the way she'd murmured, 'Such a brave man,' of Doug's boast about being allowed to witness the twins' delivery.

He wouldn't have told her that he fainted ten minutes into the last stage of labour.

'And how long did your so-convenient fling with Nerine go on?'

'Only until Baz Fuller moved in. He was a much better prospect, heading for great things. Unlike yours truly.'

Trying to make me feel sorry for him again. I said, 'Spare me the self-pity. Baz Fuller took the gap into top management that you were desperate for, but didn't make because you weren't good enough.'

'He was a devious little shit who shafted me.'

'And she dumped you for him. That makes me feel a lot better.'

He didn't answer straight away. Then he said, 'You've forgotten that it was a tough time for me, made worse when you insisted on buying the big house. I was in constant terror that we'd fall behind on the mortgage payments.'

This was really rich. I jeered, 'No, I haven't forgotten. You have. I was there for you, Doug. I thought, like a fool, that the income my columns brought in would help with the mortgage payments and set your mind at rest. Not send you out looking for consolation with other women.'

He said, 'I've told you that I just answered signals – and never if I thought you'd find out.'

'So you didn't go for any of my friends?' He turned his face away again and I felt a dreadful yawning inside. 'Oh. Which ones?'

'You don't want to know.'

'Who?' I insisted. 'You owe me, Doug. True confessions.'

After a long time and with great reluctance he muttered, 'Ginger. And later Vron.'

Betrayal piled on betrayal. He'd stood between them for Zeke's photograph of the barbecue to celebrate his thirty-fifth birthday and our tenth anniversary. Ginger Griffin with her goldfish hair and pearly skin, the arts editor with the temperament of a piranha. And tall thin clever Veronica, my divorced school friend who'd told me recently that she was seeing a married man.

'Are you still in contact with any of them?'

'You have to be joking.' He turned back with a grimace of pain that would have made my heart melt at any other time. 'I haven't touched anyone but you since we left England, and our pathetic attempts since the operation haven't been much fun.'

'I tried.'

'We both tried but the spark isn't there any more, is it? Losing a prostate is fit punishment for a philanderer. You'd better find yourself a lover, Annie.'

'And take on another devious bastard? No way.'

He said, 'When this Rigby Vale job came along, I thought I'd finally made it to breadwinner. End of complications. Home and dry at last. Fat bloody hope.'

He was trying to soften me up again. I needled, 'Your thing with Ginger. Was it before or after Zeke?'

He looked evasive. 'Oh, at odd times. I can't remember. It wasn't important. None of them ever were.'

Them. How many unadmitted infidelities were there? But I didn't want to hear now. It was the brutal fact and the treachery that were hard to bear, not how many 'odd times'. I had to face a more daunting possibility too. Ginger and Vron had drifted away into other lives, so I could learn to deal with their betrayals, but there were valued friends I still kept in touch with.

I whispered, dreading his answer, 'Susie? Cuckoo?'

He gave me a weary look. 'Neither. I'm not a complete shit. Nor am I a satyr, which you're obviously leading up to. I've never slept around, just here and there when I needed undemanding affection.'

'Affection! That's a laugh. You could have passed on a venereal disease.' I was close to tears now, wrung out by the thought of my Doug's body locked round other women. I'd thought he loved me, only me.

He leant towards me. 'Please don't over-dramatise this awful business. I've had a few encounters, odd episodes, never long-term.'

'You think you're a bloody Don Juan.'

'I'm just a normal man,' he protested. 'All this was a long time ago. I regret it with all my heart.'

'Regret betraying me or fornicating with my friends?'

His expression was abject, like a pleading dog's. 'I didn't do it to hurt you. I just got carried away sometimes.'

I struggled to my feet and blazed at him, 'Carried away! You miserable sod. It's too late to say sorry. The damage is done. You've trashed our marriage.'

His eyes closed and he seemed to sink into himself. Giving up. He mumbled, 'I really mean it. I'm sorry. But I can't go on saying so,' and collapsed against his pillows.

'Doug!'

But he had passed out. After covering him with a blanket, I went upstairs and got into bed and cried my eyes out for the Annie I would never be again. And for my inconstant lover.

We kept going like this for nearly a month: Doug struggling with the after-effects of chemo, me being stoic, Alex trying to still the troubled waters between us. The executive chairman of Rigby Vale had a letter delivered offering Doug a generous retirement package, 'For health reasons'. We'd be allowed to stay on in the house for six months.

'Health!' he raged. 'I should be so lucky.'

Alex said, 'Take the package, Doug. It's well meant and provides you with an excellent pension that devolves on Annie in time.' He didn't have to say that the time would be short. We all knew by then. He added, 'They really value the effort and the skill you've put in here.'

'I'm not completely moribund yet.'

Alex, dear kind Alex, looked at the pale shadow of his friend slumped on the sofa and said, 'Of course not. But they need to keep the place running and it's hard going without you. They're talking about finding two managers to do your job, did you know?'

'Indispensable, that's good old Doug Perceval.'

Whatever Alex thought about our ongoing hostilities, he gave us total support during that desperate time. He and the children and Mum were my anchors during Doug's last few months.

# 39

The publisher was furious when I withdrew *True Blue Superglue* and made me pay the costs of setting it. He was a canny man with good instincts that had made him rich. I also told him that I wouldn't be writing any more handbooks.

He said in his blunt way at the end of our last phone call, 'You're a bloody fool, Anne. All your books have been good sellers. People yearn for the old-fashioned virtues in our chancy world.'

'They don't exist any more.'

'That sounds unduly cynical.'

'Realistic, I'd call it.'

'Are you sure you can't tell me why you've backed out?'

'Personal reasons.'

'Ah. I know your husband's ill. Did he object, perhaps?'

'No. It's me. When I got the proof copy …' That terrible day. Doug saying, 'Fidelity is fine as an ideal but hard to maintain in the real world.'

'Are you there?' The publisher was tapping his receiver.

'Yes.' I marshalled the arguments I had prepared. 'When

I got the proof copy and read it over, it sounded false. Even worse, untrue. I don't want to feel guilty about propagating untruths to gullible readers.'

'That's a bit harsh,' he protested.

'But it's how I feel. I'm retiring for good from motivational books. Think I'll write novels instead. Satires, maybe.'

Satires. Satyrs. I could do a juicy bodice-ripper full of randy husbands and false friends.

'Anne? Don't get too carried away, whatever the crisis you're facing. You're a damn good writer. I hate to lose you.'

One fan, at least. 'Thanks.'

'And give me a ring if you change your mind. I'll keep *True Blue* on the computer, in case.'

'Please don't. Just delete it.'

'If you say so.' He sounded dubious.

'It's my copyright and I deeply regret writing it.'

'You may feel differently one day.'

'Never. It was misconceived. But thanks for your support over the years. I appreciate what you've done for me.'

'My pleasure,' he said in a voice that didn't mean it, and rang off.

'You're a fool to dump the book,' was Doug's almost identical comment when I told him. 'Just publish it under a nom de plume.'

'I can't do that. Bits have appeared in Annie Butterfield and readers will recognise them. Besides, I'm not going to propagate myths about happy marriages. I'd be a hypocrite.'

'One erring husband doesn't mean they all are.'

'Convince me, Romeo.'

'That'd be impossible in your current state of mind.'

'It's not going to change.'

He said, 'Convictions aside, you shouldn't have alienated a source of income. You'll need it when I go.'

Fishing for sympathy again. I snapped, 'You're not going. You'll survive this, though I don't know if I will.'

He was looking a bit better, Alex and I convinced ourselves. He could walk round the garden, though I made him sleep in the spare room except when the children were home and we kept up a united, if chilly, front.

'Don't be taken in by my burst of hectic activity.' He had begun to speak like this all the time, tongue in cheek, using cynicism as a defence against the realities of battling cancer. 'I feel bloody awful and know I won't make it. But you're a survivor. Women are better at it than men. You have work to do. What are you writing about now?'

'You.'

'Don't be too cruel.'

'It's rather late to say that. Serial betrayal isn't a pleasant subject.'

There was a long silence. We were sitting out on the patio in the last rays of afternoon sunshine.

After spending time with Doug every day during their vacations, Tasha had gone back to Stellenbosch and Chloe to UCT.

Robin had flown off with a team of irrigation experts invited to Abu Dhabi in the Persian Gulf by its ruling sheik, who wanted to turn his desert city into a vast garden. They telephoned often. All three seemed happy with their lives and choices.

Budgie called too. Her latest news was that her publisher wanted more spy thrillers and was putting it about that Victor B Smail was a recluse on a remote Scottish island. To her huge delight, a well-known journalist had set off to hunt 'him' down.

'Never thought I'd be a wild goose,' was her gleeful comment. 'Wonder how long it'll take him not to find me. How's the Boss today?'

'Holding his own,' I'd lied.

I was watching a ruffle of wind on the lake and thinking about Budgie when Doug said, 'Will there come a time when I'll be forgiven?'

'Probably not.'

After another long pause he said, 'Where did we go wrong, Annie? Was it your blind belief in *Candide*'s "All is for the best, in the best of possible worlds", or my inability to deal with failure?'

The look on his sunken face was so sad that I admitted, 'We were both at fault. And you had a lot of bad luck.'

'You've always been too charitable. Typical of blind believers.'

'I'm not blind.'

'Unseeing, then. Demonstrated by the facts of the matter. QED.'

'That's worse than treacherous?' Even in those last days I struggled with the idea of forgiveness.

'You said we were both at fault,' he threw back at me.

'Some failings are more heinous.'

'Heinous. Where did you dredge up that clunker? From

one of those worthy books called *Improve Your English in Eight Weeks*?'

'Books like that kept us going.'

'Which I couldn't do in the style to which you were accustomed. Though you did have me on call sometimes as a house-husband. That must count for something.' His wet-slate eyes dulled to granite.

'You're not being fair to either of us, Doug.'

'Life's not bloody fair. It's the first thing you should teach kids, before they get confused by false notions like justice and equality.'

The once-beautiful curving mouth was drawn down at both ends. And I realised that we were wiping out nearly three decades of a marriage that had been mostly good – if never as perfect as I'd foolishly believed – in a duelling month of angry retaliation. The proportion was all wrong. And we were wasting precious time.

I got up then and put my arms round him, and we both wept.

It was the last time we sat together on the patio. The weather turned cold and windy the next day and Doug was too thin to sit outside. He collapsed again a few weeks later and went downhill fast as the resurgent cancer spread from his bladder into his spine and pelvis. The pain was excruciating until we moved him to a private room in a hospice where he was given drugs that made him woozy, but still able to communicate. I stayed with him, catnapping on the twin bed when he dozed. The hospice sisters were magnificent, attending to both of us with loving care and soothing our fears with a calm acceptance of death as a natural process that made the ordeal easier to bear.

The children came home for his last weeks, and took turns with Alex to be with us. Susie and Xavier flew out too, our good friends for so many years, with their two blond boys. The hospice served tea to visitors to encourage a sociable atmosphere and there were moments when I felt as though we were in a golden bubble of time outside reality, enjoyably chatting as Doug listened with a benign smile, propped up by pillows.

The abrasive cynicism had faded to mumbled attempts at humour like, 'I never realised that casting off would be so damn simple,' and, 'Kiss me Annie, Hardy isn't available,' which I knew he intended as comfort. We said our goodbyes during that time, before his mind blurred and he began to ramble about rowing and rotgut rum. Once he said quite clearly, 'Don't forget the poor old Austin, she needs spit and polish. Tell Robin. He's a good man.' Robin wept when he heard.

Doug slipped away one evening with us all holding hands round his bed. When he had gone, the children and Mum and I kissed him and Alex bent over him too saying, 'Farewell, my dear friend.'

I would move soon to a house round the corner from Mum, who continues to study and paint while I work on this book.

'It took me a whole lifetime to discover who I am and what I really want to do,' she said once, 'and I miss your father more than I can say. For so long we lived parallel lives. It was only when he retired that we found the spark that— '

'Spare me the gory details,' I put in quickly. 'And I miss the rumpty-tumpty too. Terribly.'

She laughed, looking twenty years younger in her smock and jeans with her hair dyed bright red. Her excuse is that she has to keep up with the other students.

'I was going to say, the spark that really matters. I married your father to get away from home and we jogged along quite well together for years. And then to my utter surprise, I fell in love with him. He came in one day and said that the fishing was off and maybe we should try something new and different. He meant in bed, and it was amazing. I think he must have been talking to one of his more experienced friends. Our parallel lives started intersecting in the most interesting ways. It was like finding a treasure trove in the backyard.'

I thought, Dad? The purveyor of pearls of wisdom, good in bed?

She said, 'You needn't look so surprised, Annie. Oldies aren't devoid of sexual desire. Maybe you should write a handbook for us.'

'I've stopped doing them. You know why.'

'That's a pity. The need is great.'

'Robin's need is greater. He's asked me to collaborate on an illustrated guide to drip irrigation for new farmers. With land restitution starting, we're going to have to teach farming skills fast. His publisher says there are plenty more to be written if I'm interested.'

I couldn't hide my pride and she laughed again, saying, 'Ah, important stuff,' before turning back to her easel.

In time there would be handbooks for Chloe too, on

endangered fish species when she broadened her degree to add marine biology. And soon Tasha would be talking about a need for children's books with fun exercises and fitness games.

'I hope you're not trying to live through their lives,' Mum warned not long ago.

'Not at all. An NGO in Gauteng wants me to write about vegetable gardening in trenches so people in townships can grow their own fresh produce. It's a job for life.'

She gave me the familiar over-the-specs look then. 'Don't discount another relationship. You're still quite young.'

'Never. I wouldn't start again now. I've learnt the hard way not to be so damn trusting that …' I couldn't go on.

She came and hugged me. 'Stop it, Annie. Just remember the good things about Doug. And that he really loved you, despite the occasional lapses.'

I try. I try.

# 40

This has been a love story with a sting in its tale. After Doug died, I remembered Budgie teasing him about being a wasp, and recalled reading about the queen bee in every slender-stemmed wasp nest who lays all the eggs. And probably prides herself on it.

But I'm determined to lead my new life with a clean slate. My aim in writing this book has been to remember, deal with my regrets and move on, storing away the good memories of Doug in a safe place to call on when I'm blue.

We scattered his ashes off Cape Point according to his wishes, and Alex held a small wake for the family at his home afterwards. Mum brought a portrait of Doug painted from a photograph and propped it on an easel so he would be with us while we spoke about him, remembering the good times.

There were bouquets of flowers from the Rigby Vale management and residents, a heart-wrenching letter from Zeke, who wrote how well he understood loss, and long phone calls from Budgie, Quince, Susie and Cuckoo. Vron sent a condolence card with a sad little message: 'I always envied your wonderful relationship with Doug. Hope you won't be too lonely now that he's gone.'

Euphemia and her boys sent a telegram from Ghana saying, 'Go well into the sunset, Mr Perceval. With our respect and mighty thanks.' I could almost hear her deep voice adding, 'And no nonsense along the way. Uh-uh!'

At the end, everybody who had loved him helped to lift me on the wings of Our Song, recorded by Robin, as we sang together to lay Doug to rest.

# Acknowledgements

My thanks to:

Fourie Botha for his enduring encouragement and staunch support

The unknown reader for the heartening report

Bronwyn McLennan for her insightful and inspiring editing from Japan

Beth (Eagle Eyes) Lindop for her expertise and close attention to the final manuscript